8/6

1/6

SOVIET GENETICS
AND WORLD SCIENCE

By the same Author

★

MAN IN THE MODERN WORLD
DEMOCRACY MARCHES
ESSAYS OF A BIOLOGIST
THE UNIQUENESS OF MAN
ESSAYS IN POPULAR SCIENCE
WHAT DARE I THINK?
A SCIENTIST AMONG THE SOVIETS
BIRD-WATCHING AND BIRD-BEHAVIOUR
T. H. HUXLEY'S DIARY OF THE VOYAGE
OF H.M.S. "RATTLESNAKE"
ON LIVING IN A REVOLUTION
AFRICA VIEW
ANTS

Professor Lysenko

SOVIET GENETICS
AND WORLD SCIENCE

Lysenko and the Meaning of Heredity

By

JULIAN HUXLEY
M.A., D.SC., F.R.S.

1949
CHATTO AND WINDUS
LONDON

Published by

CHATTO & WINDUS
LONDON

CONTENTS

PREFACE

My reason for writing this book is that I believe in science and the scientific method as indispensable tools for human advance. I found so much misapprehension, even among professional scientists, about the controversy over Soviet genetics that I volunteered to write an article on the subject for the British scientific weekly, *Nature*, pointing out what seemed to me to be the major issues involved. While engaged on this, I received a letter from Mr. Schuman asking whether I would undertake the writing of a short book on the subject, and it seemed well worth while to utilize the material I had already digested, by amplifying it in book form.

I must confess that the task has been much more arduous than I anticipated, and has involved the consideration of various general questions, in addition to the actual Lysenko controversy. I can only hope that the result will be of some use in clarifying the problem of the role of science and the scientific method in world civilization, as well as the issues of the controversy itself.

I have for many years been professionally concerned with genetics and evolution, from my school-days 45 years ago when I had to master elementary Mendelism for my scholarship examination, through the period when I was responsible for the teaching of genetics in various Universities, to the present decade when I set out to write a comprehensive book on evolution, including its genetical basis. I have done my best to popularize genetics and evolutionary science, notably in collaboration with H. G. and G. P. Wells in the *Science of Life* ; and for the last three years I have been professionally concerned, as Director-General of Unesco, with science as an international activity. I had the unusual opportunity of hearing Lysenko lecture and of a conversation with him, in 1945 ; and have now read all the main documents concerning the recent genetics controversy in the U.S.S.R.

I at first imagined that there must be something in Lysenko's claims. However, the more I heard and read, the clearer it became that Lysenko and his followers are not scientific in any proper sense of the word—they do not adhere to recognized scientific method, or employ normal scientific precautions, or publish their results in a way which renders their scientific evaluation possible. They move in a different world of ideas from that of professional scientists, and do not carry on discussion in a scientific way. Michurinism, as their form of genetics is called, is largely based on ancient superstitions which the advance of scientific knowledge has left behind; in any event, it is less a branch of science comprising a basis of facts, than a branch of ideology, a doctrine which it is sought to impose upon facts. I have tried to convey this by direct quotations from their published utterances and writings.

Meanwhile Lysenko's alleged results are suspect because of his faulty methods. It may be that he has made some new discoveries: but that we cannot know until his experiments have been repeated with proper scientific precautions.

The next question was why had Lysenko won his battle and how was it possible for the Academy of Sciences to have lent their scientific authority to the suppression of an entire branch of science? The conclusion is inescapable that this has been done on ideological grounds, under political pressure, although the precise reasons why political and ideological pressure has been so forcibly exerted are not altogether clear.

In any event, it speedily became clear, that the major issue at stake was not the truth or falsity of Lysenko's claims, but the overriding of science by ideological and political authority.

The Communist Party has officially pronounced that Michurinism is scientifically true and Mendelism scientifically untrue. It has divided science into Soviet science, which is good and right, and bourgeois science, which must be combated by all Soviet scientists. Such a course of action, in my view and that of the overwhelming majority of scientists, is impermissible. To do this is to destroy the necessary autonomy and unity of science as a major human activity. This repudiation of the validity of science and scientific method, is a denial of that freedom of the intellect which we fondly imagined had been laboriously won during the past three or four centuries. This point too I have substantiated wherever possible by actual quotations.

I was finally led to a consideration of the relations between science and society in other countries and at other periods. It is clear that science is often in conflict with society or with powerful groups or vested interests in society. Sometimes science seems to threaten social stability, at others to run counter to the dominant aims of society. The problem is how to reconcile the autonomy of science with the needs of society as a whole. It is not always easy ; but it must be done if we are to enjoy the benefits which science alone can bring to society.

It is with such considerations in mind that I have written the following pages. If I criticize the actions or utterances of Soviet individuals or organizations, this is not on account of any political bias, but because I believe that they are wrong or inexpedient. As a matter of fact, I have been very appreciative of the efforts and achievements of the U.S.S.R., especially since my first visit to the country in 1932. But appreciation does not exclude criticism; and as a scientist and a believer in internationalism, I cannot help being critical of many aspects of the genetics controversy.

Many colleagues have helped me in preparing this book: I should like especially to thank Professor H. J. Muller, Professor Eric Ashby, and Dr. Cyril Darlington. I must also thank Mr. John Langdon-Davies for letting me see advance proofs of his interesting book, *Russia Puts the Clock Back*, which treats of the same controversy, but from a slightly different angle.

CHAPTER 1

THE CONTROVERSY, ITS NATURE AND HISTORY

MOST people are now aware that something has recently happened to science in the U.S.S.R., and that this something is quite important.   But there is still a great deal of misapprehension on the subject, not merely as regards specific points, but as to what the dispute is really about, and what are the essential issues involved. This is not surprising, for the whole controversy has been obscured by a fog of misunderstanding, largely resulting from the emotional smoke-screen that seems inevitably to envelop any issue concerning the U.S.S.R. Red-baiters have used it as a convenient new stick to beat the Russians with.   Communists talk of the resistance of bourgeois science to new ideas. Upholders of free enterprise say " see what happens to science under planning." Believers in state planning point to the necessity for some generally accepted doctrine, including scientific doctrine, to unify society. Pink sympathizers, while avoiding the main issue, make excuses for the Russians' action, or point to the fact that science in western countries does not enjoy complete freedom.   Libertarians let their indignation get the better of them, and confuse the rightness or wrongness of Lysenko's theories with the rightness or wrongness of the drastic methods used to defeat his opponents.   Too often, the upholders of one view are ignorant of the different atmosphere of ideas inhabited by their antagonists, and invective has too often taken the place of argument.

The best way to begin dispelling this fog of misunderstanding will be to explain the basis of the controversy and to give the history of what has happened. Later, the main issued involved can be defined ; and finally the whole controversy discussed in relation to its general social and intellectual background.

The controversy, then, primarily concerns that branch of science known as genetics. Genetics in the restricted sense deals with the way the inherited characteristics of organisms—plants and animals and human beings—are transmitted from one generation to the next. But here we have to do with genetics in the extended sense of evolutionary genetics, which deals also with the way in which organisms change their inherited characteristics in the course of many generations. Such an extension is natural and inevitable, for evolution clearly depends on heredity : the methods by which the visible characters of organisms are transmitted from one generation to the next must to a considerable extent determine the methods by which they change in the course of many generations.

The two rival systems are usually called neo-Mendelism on the one hand, and Michurinism on the other.[1] In a later chapter, I shall give a more extended description and analysis of neo-Mendelism and Michurinism from the point of view of their scientific validity.

[1] Neo-Mendelism as generally used applies only to genetics in the restricted sense, of transmission, while neo-Darwinism is used to cover evolutionary change arising from Mendelism plus natural selection. Most western scientists actually use the general phrase " evolutionary genetics " instead of neo-Darwinism. But the fact that the Russians have propounded a wholly different system of genetics makes it necessary to use a distinct term in discussing the controversial issues, and I shall for the present stick to *neo-Mendelism*. Eventually I shall have occasion to point out that the two systems have quite different natures : neo-Mendelian (neo-Darwinian) genetics is a *branch of science*, while Michurinism is primarily a *doctrine* which its adherents are attempting to impose on scientific fact.

Here I shall confine myself to a brief sketch of their fundamental characteristics, and some points concerning their historical development.

Neo-Mendelism is a generalized extension of the discovery by the Abbé Mendel, over 80 years ago, that when different kinds of peas were crossed, certain of their characters retained their distinctiveness in later generations without any trace of dilution or blending, and behaved as if they were transmitted by some kind of definite unit or particle in the reproductive cells, i.e., that the material basis of their heredity was particulate. Neo-Mendelism is the general science of particulate heredity. It has demonstrated that the hereditary units postulated by Mendel do actually exist. We now call them *genes*, and define or describe them as self-reproducing units of living matter. Each kind of gene may exist in a number of different forms, called *allels* (or alleles). The genetic difference between tallness and dwarfness in Mendel's peas was due to difference between two allels of the same kind of gene.

But it has gone much further : it has discovered that in all types of organisms so far investigated—insects, flowering plants, birds, crustacea, many protozoa, fungi, mammals (including man), ferns, etc.—there exists a material basis for inheritance, a special organ of heredity. This is constituted by the total assemblage of genes (which in higher animals, must amount to several thousand different kinds). Furthermore, the genes are arranged in a definite linear order within the cell-organs called chromosomes ;[1] their number is

[1] It has recently been discovered that a small portion of hereditary transmission is sometimes effected by something other than the ordinary genes in the chromosomes ; but this " something " appears also to be particulate, in the shape of super-molecules or other self-reproducing units in the general protoplasm (cytoplasm) of the reproductive cells. These units have been called *plasmagenes*. They appear to differ from

also kept constant (usually two of each kind of gene in each cell). The whole system is thus extremely complex and very highly organized—as we would expect if it has to discharge the varied and delicate functions demanded of an organ of heredity.

What are generally called the laws of heredity, including Mendel's original two laws, are really laws concerning the distribution of different genes from one generation to the next : they are all explicable on the basis of facts concerning the manoeuvres and behaviour of the chromosomes in cell-division and reproduction, which can be observed through the microscope.

The chromosomes are thus a distributing mechanism in heredity. The organ of heredity has other functions to perform, notably to influence and regulate the processes of development, whereby the egg or spore develops into the adult animal or plant. For instance, certain differences between a pug-dog and a greyhound, or between a typical negro and a typical white man, must somehow depend on the influence of the genes concerned on the processes leading to the development of the face and skull. This regulating or controlling function of the organ of heredity is a much more complicated subject than its distributive function, and much more difficult to investigate, and science is still only making a beginning with it. But facts about it are being discovered (e.g. that many genes affect the *rate of* developmental processes) and we can look forward to reaching various general laws and principles within a few decades. However, the extent of our

ordinary genes mainly in the fact that, since they are not arranged in single file within the chromosomes, an indefinite instead of a fixed number of them can be present in each cell, and their distribution cannot be orderly and regular like that of ordinary genes.

ignorance must not be allowed to obscure the achievements already made by neo-Mendelian genetics. And its chief achievement is the discovery of the physical basis of heredity. There does exist a specific organ of heredity, as there are specific organs of digestion, or of bodily movement; and it is just as distinct and separate from other organs as are the stomach or the skeletal muscles, although, being microscopic, it is not so obvious.

This discovery of the organ of heredity and of the fact that it is built up out of genes is as important as was the discovery of molecules and the fact that they are built up out of atoms.

Outside the U.S.S.R., neo-Mendelism is usually equated with genetics, since all but a negligible few of Western geneticists (and, up till last year, a considerable number of Soviet geneticists) have become satisfied that the machinery of heredity is wholly (or, to be on the safe side, almost wholly) particulate.

Neo-Mendelism is the science of variation as well as of heredity. It has established, in the first place, that the visible variation of organisms (for instance variation in human skin-colour or in the size of pigs) can be separated into two components of basically different origin—those which are due to differences in the hereditary constitution and those which are not. The latter we call *modifications*. Modifications are of two somewhat distinct sorts, the one due to differences in environment, such as the darker skin-colour of white men who have been exposed to plenty of sun, the other due to differences in habits or activity, such as the greater muscular development that comes with heavy work. But all modifications have this in common, that in the first instance they affect the individual body and its organs, and not the reproductive cells.

In the second place, neo-Mendelism has established that the variations originating in the heredity constitution are due to *mutations*. A mutation is a change of measurable extent in the constitution—either a change in quality of a single gene, or a change in quantity due to the addition or subtraction of whole genes, sections of chromosomes, whole chromosomes, or whole chromosome-sets. A small part of this sort of variation, as it exists at any one moment, is due to fresh mutations, but most of it is due to old mutations (giving rise to mutant genes which have then become stored in the hereditary constitution), and to their combination of mutated genes with each other and with unmutated genes. The existence difference between a natural blonde and a natural brunette depends on a difference in a few kinds of genes, blondes and brunettes possessing different allels of these genes. But it is of mutational origin, due to some of the original allels having mutated into slightly different ones; and this holds good even though the blonde, through modifications acquired by intensive sun-bathing, might become as dark as the brunette.

Here I must diverge a moment to clear up a common misunderstanding, that neo-Mendelism denies any influence to the environment. On the contrary, it starts from the principle, solidly established by fifty years of research, that all characters of adult organisms are always the result of the interaction of heredity and environment. The hereditary constitution (the genes) is a chemical system which reacts with its environment during development to produce certain results. Alter either, and the end-result may alter.

For instance, there are breeds of fowls which breed true for yellow legs and others which breed true for white legs. This difference is due to difference between the allels of a single gene, as is shown by crossing the two types and breeding a second generation, when yellow and white " segregate " in the typical 3:1 Mendelian ratio. But this only holds good if they are fed on a normal diet. If they are given only white maize, birds of the normally yellow-legged breed will have white legs. To show yellow, their genes have to interact with a chemical substance found in yellow maize (and also in green vegetables), but not in white maize. Or again, dwarfness in pea plants may be due to bad conditions, *or* to a single gene : only experiment can decide which, in any particular instance.

The situation is in principle similar to what happens with lifeless chemical substances, though much more complicated in detail. For instance, the hydrocarbon octane (well known in octane petrol) differs from heptane merely by having 8 carbon and 18 hydrogen atoms instead of 7 and 16 respectively. It " reacts with its environment " differently, in that it boils at a higher temperature when heated. But the precise temperature depends on other conditions in the environment, notably pressure. At a reduced pressure, octane will boil at the same temperature as heptane will at normal atmospheric pressure.

In genetics, the complexity of the interaction is at its greatest in regard to human mental characters. The actual degree of intellectual attainment, for instance, is always in part—sometimes in large part—due to opportunity and education ; but it also depends in part on genetic make-up. If you cannot get figs from thistles, you also cannot get good figs without good environment.

In all the problems which genetics faces, one of its

first tasks is to try to disentangle differences due to environments from differences due to heredity. In many cases, this can only be done by experiment (or to a certain extent by mathematical analysis).

Mutations are in general produced either as a spontaneous rearrangement of the structure of a gene, or as the result of some agency such as X-rays, ultra-violet radiation, or certain chemical substances acting on the gene. In all cases (with a few possible exceptions), the change produced by a mutation bears no special relation to the agency producing it. Thus a well-known mutation changing red to white eyes in fruit-flies is not produced by anything to do with vision, but by X-rays (or other agencies) hitting a particular gene and producing a rearrangement of its atomic structure and turning it into a new allel. Furthermore, although there are normally two representatives of each kind of gene in each cell (sometimes both the same allel, sometimes two different allels), only one mutates at any one time : the fact that both do not mutate together thus seems to rule out any idea that mutation is due to the effect of general conditions, and to confirm that it depends on agencies capable of acting on the atomic structure of single genes.

Neo-Mendelism has also established that, at least in the great majority of cases, and possibly always, modifications are not inherited. Whether a woman had grown brown by constant sun-bathing or had kept out of the sun and stayed very blonde, would make no difference to the skin-colour of her children.

This being so, it follows that neither the effects of use or disuse or of alterations in the conditions of the environment can normally play any direct role in evolution. Evolution consists in a change in the hereditary constitution, and neo-Mendelism in the extended sense has established that this is brought about by natural selection favouring the possessors of certain genes and certain mutations as against others, thus producing a differential survival of certain types. The black skin of negroes is thus not due to the accumulation of the effects of tanning by the sun over many generations, but to the natural selection, in tropical regions, of those individuals who are naturally darker-skinned owing to their hereditary constitution. Selection will favour these, since their black pigment prevents the undue amount of ultra-violet in the tropical sunlight from penetrating the skin and damaging the underlying tissues. Even a very small selective advantage in each generation will produce large changes in evolution over a period of time which is, biologically speaking, quite short.

Evolution is normally adaptive, in the sense that the animals and plants which it produces are adjusted, often with astonishing delicacy, to their environment and their conditions of life. Adaptation is apparently purposeful ; but one of the major achievements of modern biology has been to show that the purpose is apparent only, and that adaptation can be accounted for on a scientific basis, as the automatic result of mutation and selection, operating over many generations. In a similar way, physical science, largely as the result of Newton's work in the 17th century, showed that the orderly movements of the heavenly bodies, which at first sight seemed to demand divine guidance, can be accounted for on a purely scientific basis, as the automatic result of the force of gravity.

Organisms are thus closely related to their environments. But the relation is not a direct one : the environment does not affect the hereditary constitution directly. It is an indirect one, mediated through the complicated and lengthy process of natural selection causing differential survival of better-adapted variants.

The theory and system of heredity that we call neo-Mendelism thus grades into the theory and system of evolution that we call neo-Darwinism. Or we might perhaps say that neo-Darwinism is neo-Mendelism plus Natural Selection.

The controversy cannot be properly understood unless we bear in mind some of the salient facts about the history of neo-Mendelism as well as its present stage of development. Mendel published his results on peas in the 1860's, but they remained virtually unnoticed until 1900, when they were brought to light, confirmed, and extended to other organisms, notably by Bateson.

When I began studying biology at Oxford in 1906, the main issue in genetics was whether Mendelian inheritance (i.e. by self-reproducing particles) applied only to a restricted range of characters and organisms, or whether it was general. By about 1910, however, it had become evident that Mendelian inheritance was general.

Meanwhile already in 1901, Sutton had pointed out that various facts of Mendelian inheritance could be at once explained if Mendel's unit-factors, or genes as we now call them, were lodged in the visible cell-organs called chromosomes. These had been discovered in the early 1880's, and a great many details of their behaviour in cell-division and sexual reproduction had been elucidated before 1900.

By about 1920, it had been proved, largely by T. H. Morgan and his school, that the genes were carried by the chromosomes, and also that they were arranged in a definite linear order in them (in 1919 Morgan wrote a book with the title " The Physical Basis of Heredity"), and it had become evident that Mendelian inheritance was not only general, but must be universal in all organisms possessing chromosomes—which means all organisms from the highest to the lowest, with the possible exception of the bacteria and viruses.

Meanwhile, the rather crude ideas of the earlier Mendelians about genes were being modified as new facts were brought to light. It was discovered that any given gene might affect a number of apparently separate visible characters, and that any given character (such as the shape of a limb or the colour of hair) was always due to the combined action of many genes. It was also discovered that the number of genes in any higher animal must be very large—of the order of several thousands. Thus geneticists abandoned any naive ideas they may have had that any one gene somehow determined or was responsible for one particular character of the adult, and came to think of the hereditary constitution as a chemical system of quite extraordinary complexity—much more complex that any other known—whose component units (the genes) were carefully adjusted so as to be able to regulate the development and working of the animal or plant.

Natural gene-mutation was early noticed, and in 1927 Muller succeeded in producing mutations artificially by X-rays.[1] Since then, a great deal has been

[1] A curious error was made by de Vries in the early 1900's. On the basis of large inherited differences in Evening Primroses, he advanced the view that evolution proceeded by large jumps, which he called *mutations*. Later research showed that these differences were not really due to mutations at all, in the sense of new changes in the hereditary constitution, but to peculiarities in the chromosome set-up of Evening Primroses. His views have now only a historical interest.

discovered as to the nature and the frequency of mutation in many organisms.

About 1920 biologists began to be interested as to how natural selection would operate on organisms with Mendelian (particulate) inheritance, and started applying mathematical methods to the problem. In 1930, R. A. Fisher laid the foundations of evolutionary genetics as a separate branch of science with his book " The Genetical Basis of Natural Selection." Since about 1935, many studies have been made establishing how particulate inheritance and selection actually operate in nature to produce changes in wild animal and plant populations. Finally, in the last decade, the first discoveries concerning the chemical nature of the genes have been made, and it has been shown that they contain mainly proteins together with a particular kind of nucleic acid. In addition, the existence of a subsidiary method of particulate inheritance, by means of plasmagenes carried in the body of cells and not in chromosomes, has been demonstrated.

Like any other branch of science, neo-Mendelism has had to develop its own special techniques and methodological precautions, which are necessary if its results are to be adjudged scientifically valid. Thus the use of genetically purified strains of animals and plants is as essential for many kinds of genetical experiments as is the use of chemically purified materials in many kinds of chemical experiments, and methods for effecting the required degree of genetical purity have been worked out. Methods have also been worked out in favourable material like fruit-flies, for producing strains with particular combinations of genes, needed to test out some new idea. I can assure my readers that, though any brief description of such methods would be incomprehensible to non-scientists (and indeed to most non-geneticists), they are both necessary and efficacious.

Mathematical methods for checking numerical results ; the proper way of using controls ; precautions for discounting unconscious selection by the experimenter or automatic selection by the environment ; the way in which results should be published so as to make it possible for others to check them—all this and much more has now been worked out, until today we can say that the methods and precautions are an integral part of neo-Mendelism as a science.

In 1902 Mendelism was a theory covering the inheritance of a few characters in a few higher plants and animals. Today it has developed into a branch of science covering the inheritance and evolution of all (or almost all) characters of all (or almost all) organisms.

I should add that the Russian upholders of Michurinism often bring Weismann and his ideas into the controversy. Weismann was a distinguished German zoologist who, towards the close of the last century, developed the idea of what is generally called the continuity of the germ-plasm. Observation through the microscope had shown that in sexual reproduction the new organism is produced by the union of two reproductive cells, the sperm from the male and the egg or ovum from the female. The result is the fertilized ovum or zygote, which then proceeds to divide into the hundreds, thousands, or millions of cells which form the adult. Most of these cells form the organs of the individual body or *soma ;* but some produce new reproductive cells, or germ-cells, which repeat the process. The lineage of cells which produces the reproductive cells is continuous through the generations, and was styled by him the *germ-plasm.* In each

generation, this throws off the soma as a sidebranch :
so there is no continuity of substance between the
soma or body of a parent and that of its offspring. He
drew the conclusion that it would be impossible for
alterations in the soma to become hereditary ; for to
do so they would have somehow to pass into the germ-
plasm, and there seemed to be no mechanism by which
this could be effected.

He also suggested a very elaborate hypothesis as to
the role of the chromosomes in heredity ; but this was
speedily disproved, and is of no relevance to the
present controversy.

Later observation has shown that the distinction
between soma and germ-plasm is not always so rigid
as Weismann supposed, especially in plants. But even
there, most tissues of the plant-body do not in fact
produce reproductive cells, so that the general distinction still holds between a continuity of substance
from generation to generation along one line of cells,
and a discontinuity of substance between the rest of
the body in one generation and the next.

In any case, Weismann's ideas in their original form,
have now been superseded by the discoveries of neo-
Mendelian genetics. These have now shown that it is
the chromosomes of the cell-lineage from fertilized egg
to reproduction cells, which constitute a continuous
germ-plasm, in the sense of a complex system of living
matter which can be continuous through the generations by virtue of its capacity for self-reproduction.
The chromosomes of the cells of the body at large are
not continuous through the generation, since there is no
way in which they or their descendants can get into
the reproductive cells. Furthermore, the system of
chromosomes has been shown to possess extraordinary

constancy of structure and properties, (which is again due to the capacity of its units to reproduce or copy themselves) and its occasional inconstancy, due to mutation, has so far been found to be quite independent of changes in the body or soma. Thus Weismann's general conclusions about the inheritance of characters acquired by the individual soma still hold, although geneticists today formulate them rather differently, pointing out that the observed facts about reproduction and the chromosome mechanism of inheritance make it extremely difficult to see how a somatic effect (say of sunlight on the colour of our skins) could find its way into the elaborately self-regulating system of self-reproducing genes. But the details of Weismannism are no longer relevant, having been superseded or swallowed up by neo-Mendelism.

Finally I must point out that neo-Mendelism is a large and complicated branch of modern science, and already the subject of many textbooks, and it is impossible for a student or for a layman starting from scratch to obtain in a few pages a really adequate account even of its main features—almost as impossible as it would be to give in a few pages an intelligible account of, say, modern European history to a visitor from another planet. All I can hope to do in a little book like this is to make some assertions about it : but these are based on forty years' professional concern with genetics, and can be verified and understood by referring to any reputable book on the subject, such as E. B. Ford's *Study of Heredity* in the Home University Library, E. Altenburg's *How We Inherit*, A. Scheinfeld's *You and Heredity*, (London and New York, 1939) or E. W. Sinnott and Dunn's large textbook, *The Principles of Genetics* (McGraw-Hill Book Co.).

Michurinism takes its name from the Russian horticulturist and plant-breeder, Michurin, who lived from 1855 to 1935. However, as a theory it has been almost entirely elaborated by Lysenko, the present President of the Lenin Academy of Agricultural Sciences, together with the philosopher Prezent and others of Lysenko's followers. It is a particular version of the general theory of evolution known as Lamarckism. In its classical form, this asserted that " acquired characters," whether due to changed environment or to use or disuse of organs, (i.e. what the neo-Mendelians call *modifications*), are inherited to a slight degree in each generation, and that they can accumulate and become fixed in the course of generations so as to produce evolutionary change.[1] In Darwin's time, nothing was known about the mechanism of heredity, not even the existence of chromosomes or the elementary facts of Mendelian inheritance. Accordingly, he accepted Lamarckism as a contributary cause of evolutionary change, although he always assigned chief importance to Natural Selection.

Michurinism is distinguished from classical Lamarckism by the following main features. In the first place, it ascribes great importance to what it calls the " shattering " or " shaking" of heredity (see Lysenko, 1948, p. 31, and my Chap. 4). By this is apparently meant the breaking down of the stability normal to the hereditary constitution, by means of various kinds of what we might call shock-treatment. Once the shattering process is effected, the heredity is supposed

[1] Lamarck himself considered that only use and disuse and the conscious efforts of organisms, had an effect on evolution, but the general theory was soon extended to include Buffon's idea, that the effects of the environment (such as the fleshiness of many plants caused by saline conditions) could also be inherited and so could contribute to evolutionary change.

to become more labile and plastic, or what Lysenko
sometimes calls " unestablished." Some of the " shattering " treatments consist in new conditions of
environment applied at special crises or phases of the
life-history. The results of these treatments are supposed to become hereditary—i.e. to have a Lamarckian
effect.

Secondly, the Michurinites employ the term *heredity*
for what Western geneticists, in order to avoid confusion
with heredity as a general process, usually call *the
hereditary constitution*. This presumably is to avoid any
idea of a specialized material basis for inheritance such
as has been discovered by neo-Mendelism. For the
Michurinites, heredity (I quote Lysenko's own words
(1948) ; and see also Lysenko, 1949) " is inherent not
only in the chromosomes, but in every particle of the
living body." What is more, it is supposed to be
a process of the same nature as ordinary metabolism,
the chemical cycle of living bodies, which involves
inter alia assimilation or the building up of simpler
substances into living matter, and dissimilation or the
subsequent breakdown of living matter into simpler
compounds. Thus Lysenko (*l.c.*) himself writes,
" Heredity is determined by the specific type of
metabolism. You need but change the type of metabolism in a living body to bring about a change in
heredity." In any event, heredity for the Michurinites
has the power of assimilation—for instance in certain
circumstances it is supposed to be able to " assimilate "
external conditions, by making their effects hereditary
and so making them a part of itself. And apparently
all of the heredity is supposed to be a result of this
process of assimilation. Thus Lysenko (*l.c.*) defines
heredity as " *the effect of the concentration of the action of*

external conditions assimilated by the organism in a series of preceding generations." (His italics).

Michurinism, even though it rejects some of the ideas of classical Lamarckism, is thus entirely Lamarckian in its general theoretical basis. This is clearly brought out by Lysenko (*l.c.*) when he writes " Changes in heredity are as a rule the result of the organisms' development *under external conditions which, to some extent or other, do not correspond to the natural requirements of the given organic form.*" (His italics) ; and even more sweepingly by his assertion that " the materialist theory of the evolution of living nature [which he has previously equated with Michurinism] involves recognition of the necessity of hereditary transmission of individual characteristics acquired by the organism under the conditions of its life ; *it is unthinkable without recognition of the inheritance of acquired characters.*" (Italics mine). As an example, he cites the vernalization of " winter " cereals i.e. making them flower earlier by treating the seeds with moisture at a low temperature so that they behave like " spring " strains (see later for a detailed description). This effect is a well-established fact as regards any single generation ; but Lysenko claims that by a modified treatment, it can be rendered hereditary, so that a winter rye, for instance, can be turned into a permanently spring type.[1]

A special feature of Michurinism as developed by Lysenko is the stress it lays on what he calls vegetative hybridization, effected by means of grafting. This is advanced as a second method, in addition to that of changing environment conditions, of " shattering "

[1] As mentioned later, other workers have not been able to confirm these results.

heredity. It is also held up as evidence that neo-Mendelism is not true.

In grafting, a *scion* or small piece of one strain, is grafted on to a rooted *stock* of another strain. It has been known for some time that scion and stock may influence one another, though this according to the experience of Western geneticists and horticulturists is unusual. However, Michurin and Lysenko claim that such effects are both large and frequent.

These effects are only modifications of the individual stocks or scions concerned. However, Lysenko also claims that grafting can also produce hereditary effects, and it is to these that the term *vegetative hybridization* is applied. According to Lysenko (*l.c.*) the " heredities " of both parties can be affected by grafting, so that " by planting the seeds from the stock or the scion it is possible to obtain offspring, individual representatives of which will possess characteristics not only of the strain from which the seed has been taken, but also of the other with which it has been united by grafting."

Furthermore, it is claimed that new combinations of the characters of the two strains used in the graft may appear in later generations obtained from the seeds of the first " graft-hybrid " generation.[1] Lysenko sums up his point of view by stating "we already have every ground to believe that every graft of a plant in its youthful stage produces changes in heredity."

The third method of " shattering " heredity according to Michurinism is (I again quote Lysenko) " by cross-breeding, particularly of forms sharply differing in habitat or origin ... The nature (heredity) of crosses, particularly in the first generation, is usually unstable,

[1] For full discussion of these results, see Chapter Three.

19

easily responding to the action of the conditions of life, feeding, and maintenance."

In point of fact, Soviet breeders have been able, so far as one can judge from the reports, to secure some valuable practical results by crossing widely distinct varieties and then selecting from among the progeny in the first and later generations. However, such results can equally well be explained on strict neo-Mendelian lines, since a hybrid between two strains differing in many genes must inevitably produce a wide range of new gene-combinations, and therefore of characters, in subsequent generations, and the best of these can then be isolated and purified by selection. The difference lies in the interpretation of the facts. For the Michurinites both the two united heredities have been " shaken " into a general condition of instability, in which they can more readily assimilate the effects of external conditions. For the neo-Mendelians, the instability and resultant wide variety of new forms produced is due to an instability in the structure of the hereditary constitution of the first-generation hybrid. Such a hybrid cannot breed true : so many of its gene-pairs are made up of widely differing gene-partners that the normal processes of Mendelian segregation cannot help but produce a very wide range of genetic variation in subsequent generations.

Michurin's own experiments in this field seem to have been conducted with fruit-trees, whose genetic behaviour is peculiar in many respects (see later, p. 93n). In any case, workers in other countries have not been able to obtain the same results.

Of these three methods of " shattering " heredity, graft-hybridization clearly cannot have played any role in natural evolution. Thus as a theory of evolution Michurinism depends on the supposed inheritance of acquired characters, produced by the effects of changed environment on the heredity when it is in a peculiarly plastic state. And this plasticity depends on the " shattering " of the heredity (much of it by amateurs and students) either by wide crosses or by the effects of changed conditions acting at special critical phases in development.

Before proceeding further, it must be pointed out that the scientific status of Michurinism is very different from neo-Mendelism. The latter incorporates large numbers of facts and laws which have been repeatedly and independently verified by scientists all over the world ; the hereditary constitution which it postulates —of large numbers of genes arranged in a regular way within chromosomes—has been established as factually true ; and its theoretical principles are all directly derivable from this central fact of a particulate constitution carried by chromosomes.

On the other hand, many of the results claimed as facts by the Michurinites (e.g. vegetative hybridization and the inheritance of acquired characters) have not proved capable of verification by scientists outside Russia ; and others (e.g. of " shattering " heredity by crossing) are equally well interpreted on Mendelian lines. Further, the Michurinites are known to have neglected many of the customary precautions taken by western geneticists to ensure the validity of their experiments, and have deliberately rejected the use of statistical analysis to check the scientific significance of their numerical results.

What is more, they have not taken the trouble to check the basic facts and principles established by fifty years of patient genetical research elsewhere, but have simply rejected them. For instance, Lysenko at one point said that evolution was " unthinkable " without the inheritance of acquired characters. To which one can only retort that he cannot have taken the trouble to read and understand recent work on neo-Darwinism, such as that of R. A. Fisher, H. J. Muller, Sewall Wright, or J. B. S. Haldane, which has firmly established that evolution is much more " thinkable " on a neo-Mendelian than on a Lamarckian basis.

We may perhaps sum up the difference between the two systems (and a very important difference it is) in the following way. Mendelism represents the coherent development of a central scientific concept, whose formulation was necessary as being the only way in which certain observed facts could be explained. (The concept was that of the unit-factor of heredity, later called the gene, and the facts were those obtained by Mendel in crossing varieties of peas). The development has consisted on the one hand in the generalization of the concept, on the other of its refinement.

It is worth pointing out that just the same kind of thing has happened in chemistry since the time of Dalton, nearly 150 years ago. Dalton's fundamental concept was of a unit-particle of matter, the atom ; and it was necessitated as the only way of interpreting the facts about pure chemical substances always combining in regular proportions by weight. All further progress in chemistry has been linked with the development of this basic concept. Dalton could no more have foreseen that atoms were composed of smaller particles, or that we today could make accurate models of the structure of complex molecules, giving the number and position of all their dozens of constituent atoms, than could Mendel have foreseen that his unit-factors were composed of protein and nucleic acid, or that accurate maps could be made of their position inside the chromosomes. But in both cases the later developments have depended on the steady generalization and refinement of a single scientific concept.

Michurinism, on the other hand, represents the promulgation of a central idea ; and this idea is *not* the only way in which the facts could be explained (since some could be equally well or better explained as due to faulty methods, and others as due to other causes.) The idea is in large measure a preconceived idea, which has been imposed on the facts instead of arising out of them ; when the facts do not fit the idea, their relevance or even their existence is denied. Unlike neo-Mendelism, it is not quantitative, so that it lacks precision. Its chief novelty, the assertion that heredity is the result of the assimilation of external influences, is based only on analogy, not on scientific experiment or observation.

This is what I meant by saying that Michurinism is a doctrine. It is an essentially non-scientific or pre-scientific doctrine applied to a branch of scientific study, not a branch of science in its own right. For this reason, it is very difficult to give any connected history of Michurinism. It is true that the pronouncements of earlier workers in the field have been pulled in, but this is chiefly to give authority to the system, not because their scientific work constitutes a stage in its development. This holds on the one hand for Russian pioneers like Michurin, since the whole tendency of the U.S.S.R. is now to magnify the contributions of Russians to scientific development, and to glorify Russian science as a national development, different from the science of non-Marxist countries ; and on the other hand for Darwin, since he is officially regarded as an authority by Marxist philosophy.[1]

In other countries, such pronouncements and detailed formulations are regarded as having only historical interest. We in the west revere Darwin as one of the great scientists of all time ; but we do not try to justify our recent conclusions by his formulations or pronouncements, for they were made the best part of a century ago, and his original ideas have either been taken over and developed, or superseded, or in some cases shown to be untrue, by the later advance of biological science.

The fullest account of Michurinism available in any western country is to be found in the summary by Hudson and Richens (1948) entitled " The New Genetics in the Soviet Union." But it is not an account of the history of the growth of a science : it resolves itself into an enumeration of the influence on the formulation of Michurinism exerted by dialectical materialism in general, and by the authority of various historical figures in particular.

The history of the actual controversy, on the other hand, can be given fairly fully. In what follows, I rely largely upon the evidence of Professor Muller (1948, and in letters). Muller in 1922 brought the first stocks of *Drosophila*, the most fruitful material for pure research in genetics, to the U.S.S.R. In the

[1] Ashby (1947), the well-known botanist who made a careful and appreciative study of Soviet science while in the U.S.S.R., writes about Michurin that he and Luther Burbank were both " clever gardeners with no rigorous scientific training ; they both ' had an eye ' for a good plant, and they achieved great success in producing new varieties . . . Both assumed that their fame would give authority to their opinions on subjects they knew nothing about ; and they both made irresponsible pronouncements about the laws of inheritance and variation."

'30's he was officially invited to advise on and to direct genetical research in the U.S.S.R., and spent several years there as Senior Geneticist in the Institute of Genetics of the U.S.S.R. Academy of Sciences. He left in 1937 after having become very disillusioned by the political control which was being exercised over genetics. In addition, I refer my readers to Dobzhansky (1949), Goldschmidt (1949), and Ashby (1946, 1947, and 1948). Dobzhansky is one of the world's leading geneticists, a Russian who was educated in the U.S.S.R., but left to take up his career in the U.S.A. as he felt there were better prospects for genetical science there. Goldschmidt, equally distinguished in genetical research, is recording what he saw as one of the three foreign guests of honour at a Russian genetics congress held in 1929. Ashby is a Professor of Botany who was a Counsellor in the Australian Legation at Moscow in 1944–1945, with the official function of reporting on Russian science and its organization.

The first point to note is that, although for a period after 1922, neo-Mendelian genetics was actively encouraged in the U.S.S.R., and some excellent research in the subject continued to be done until 1948, yet it soon began to meet with hostility, not from other scientists, but from political quarters. The probable reasons for this hostility I shall discuss in detail in a later chapter. Here I will merely say that many of the political and ideological leaders seem to have wanted a theory of biological and human heredity which assigned the chief role in evolution to environment, and to have disliked the idea, which was implicit in neo-Mendelism, of large innate differences necessarily existing between individuals. One of the first signs of this preference for a Lamarckian theory had to do with Kammerer. Kammerer was an Austrian biologist, or rather naturalist, who had put forward spectacular claims to have induced the inheritance of acquired characters in salamanders and toads. It was eventually found that some of the crucial specimens had been faked, and in any case nobody else was able to obtain similar results, so that his claims were soon entirely discredited.

However, Lunacharsky, the very able Commissar for Education at the time, was so possessed with the idea that Lamarckism must be right, and Mendelian genetics wrong and a bourgeois invention to boot, that he took the trouble to arrange for the production of a film, written by himself, glorifying Kammerer and putting down the faking to the machinations of reactionary enemies of true science. Goldschmidt himself saw the film at the Congress I have mentioned, in 1929.[1]

It was not till 1932 or 1933, however, that Mendelian genetics began to suffer. Individual geneticists began to lose their jobs, some being banished to Siberia, others sent to labour camps, others just disappearing. Chetverikov, Ferry, Ephroimson, Levitsky, and Agol were among the neo-Mendelians thus dealt with before 1934. The first accusations that neo-Mendelism was " idealist "—a grave sin in the light of Marxist ideology —date from about 1935, and it was on this ground that

[1] It is worth while noting that Professor J. B. S. Haldane, in his *Science and Everyday Life* (1939), took precisely the opposite view of the ideological implications of Lamarckism. He wrote, " reactionary biologists, such as Professor MacBride, who thinks that the unemployed should be sterilized, naturally use the theory of the transmission of acquired habits for political ends. It is silly, they say, to expect the children of manual workers to take up book-learning, or those of long-oppressed races to govern themselves."

Agol was "liquidated" in 1936. Muller (1948) continues, "In 1936, the Medico-genetical Institute, which, with its numerous staff of biologists, psychologists and more than 200 physicians, constituted a shining example, unmatched anywhere in the world, of the possibilities of research in human genetics, was vilified and misrepresented in *Pravda*, and then dissolved. One of the charges made against the Institute was that it had been attempting to exalt heredity as against environment. Everyone conversant with the Institute's work knows that actually it had been entirely objective in its gathering of data, but that in its interpretations it had leaned as far as possible—if not even too far—in the environmentalist direction. Under pressure Solomon Levit, founder and director of the Institute, made a " confession " of scientific guilt, which he later admitted to the writer was entirely false and given only because loyalty to the Communist Party demanded it. Immediately afterwards he was abstracted from the scene, and has not been heard from since."

The International Congresses of Genetics are the most important gatherings of geneticists. This did not prevent the Russian authorities in 1936 from calling off the 7th Congress, which had been scheduled to be held at Moscow in 1937. As Muller writes, " This meeting was called off after the Party had first toyed with the idea of allowing it to be held with the provision that all papers on evolution and human genetics be omitted—in spite of the fact that many foreign geneticists had intended in their papers to attack the Nazi racist doctrines ! In 1939, when Edinburgh finally acted as host to the Congress, all forty Soviet geneticists who had submitted papers to it were at the last moment refused permission to attend. At the same

27

time the world-renowned and widely-beloved president of the Congress, Nicolai Ivanovich Vavilov, the Soviet's leading bona fide geneticist, sent to Edinburgh a discourteous letter of resignation, which, according to information in my possession had been written for him."

Meanwhile, two other significant things had happened. The exaltation of Lysenko, as chief opponent of neo-Mendelian genetics, had begun, and special conferences were staged in Russia to discuss the rival merits of neo-Mendelism and Michurinism. The first of these was held in 1936, in place of the International Congress that was concelled. It was carefully pre-arranged and widely publicized as an important controversy. The discussion took place before a large audience of specially invited spectators, and it seems that this was the first occasion on which dialectical materialism and Marxist ideology were utilized on a large scale to justify Michurinism and discredit Mendelism. Lysenko spoke as the main representative of Michurinism. Muller was working in the U.S.S.R. during this period, and was among the speakers, so that his account of the proceedings and their aftermath is very valuable. He states that the Conference was presided over by Communist Party administrators.

At this Conference, it was clear that the scientists in general sided with the neo-Mendelians, in spite of violent attacks on them in the press. Accordingly, many of the speeches were heavily expurgated before the proceedings were published in book form; and within a few months the book was placed on the banned list.

A second " genetics controversy " was staged in 1939. Perusal of the proceedings (see [5])[1] shows that by now

[1] See list of literature cited. Figures refer to summaries and reports; individual contributions are cited alphabetically by author and date.

the attack had been much intensified. As Muller writes, " this time the Lysenkoists were made to appear as clear-cut victors," while the Mendelians were publicly denounced and shamed.

The career of Lysenko is summarized by Hudson and Richens (1946, p.15 ff.). Lysenko, born in 1898, had begun to come into prominence about 1929, but at first only in relation to botanical theories, such as that of phasic development, and to agricultural practices, such as that of vernalization, which had nothing to do with genetics or evolution. In 1935, in a book which he published in conjunction with the philosopher Prezent, he made his first attack on classical genetics in general and neo-Mendelism in particular, and in the same year he launched a new journal, *Jarovizacija*, to disseminate his views ; including the thesis that the effects of environment could be inherited.

It was soon evident that he enjoyed considerable official backing among political circles. At the 1936 Conference, he began to attack various aspects of Mendelism, including such well-established facts as Mendelian segregation, pure lines, and transgressive variation of hybrids in the F_2 generation, and questioned the significance of chromosomes and genes in heredity.

From 1935 on, he enlisted the press in support of his views, and became more important as a public figure. He entered political life, and was for a time a Vice-President of the Supreme Soviet. He has been twice awarded a Stalin Prize, has received the Order of Lenin, and was made a Hero of the Soviet Union in May, 1941. In 1938 he was elected President of the Lenin Academy of Agricultural Sciences, a position previously held by his rival Vavilov. He later replaced Vavilov in other posts.

In 1940 he began attacking the use of statistical methods, and of mathematics in general, in biology, and started urging that neo-Mendelism should be barred from educational curricula. From this period there date his first claims that heredity can be altered by grafting (" vegetative hybridization "), and the development of his special theory that heredity is in some unexplained way the result of the " assimilation " of external conditions by the organism over a series of generations.

From the time of the first " genetics controversy " in 1936, and to a still greater extent after the second in 1939, Mendelian geneticists were subjected to attack. Before the end of the war, a number of the most distinguished Mendelians had disappeared from the scene, including men of international repute like Karpechenko, Serebrovsky and Vavilov. Owing to the rigorous censorship on news leaving the country, we know next to nothing of the details of the fate of most of them. But of the most distinguished of all, Vavilov, we do know something.

N. I. Vavilov had travelled widely, and as a young man had worked under Bateson in England. He had published a good deal of valuable research before the Revolution. He was early appointed head of the All-Union Institute of Plant Industry, and a little later succeeded Philipchenko in control of the Bureau (later called *Institute*) of Genetics under the Academy of Sciences. His work came to the notice of Lenin, who, when he set up the Lenin Academy of Agricultural Sciences, put Vavilov at its head.

He organized a series of expeditions to regions where various crop-plants were presumed to have originated— Abyssinia, Mexico and Central America, Afghanistan, the South American Andes—and, as Darlington (1947) writes " his collections put all our ideas of the origins of cultivated plants in a new light. They also enabled Soviet breeders to work with the best possible materials in improving the crop plants needed for the new agricultural development of their country "—since his collections consisted largely of living strains of plants, from which, by appropriate crossing according to Mendelian methods, favourable genes could be introduced into the strains of crop-plants used in Russia.

I saw a good deal of Vavilov when I first visited the U.S.S.R. in 1932, and can testify to his energy and ability and the value of his work. He was devoted to his science and to the ideal of practical improvement in Russian agriculture. His collections, both of dried material and of living strains, were unique in their range and variety. His reputation as a scientist was so great that in 1942 the Royal Society of England conferred on him the highest distinction which it can bestow on a man of science from another country, by electing him a Foreign Member (the total number of Foreign Members, from all countries and in all branches of science, is limited to fifty).

Meanwhile, however, though the Royal Society knew next to nothing about it at the time, Vavilov had been disgraced. Attacks on some of his views had begun quite early. In 1936, an agriculturalist called Kolj published a virulent (and ignorant) onslaught on him in which (I quote Hudson and Richens) " he was accused of having failed in his duty of applying genetics to the practical problems of crop improvement, of having sent worthless expeditions to collect material for his World Collection instead of concentrating on local varieties, of being more interested in formal genetics than practical application, of showing a suspicious friendliness to genetical ideas emanating from fascist Germany, and of being unsympathetic to the theories of Michurin and Lysenko ". In fact Kolj was already practising all the unscrupulous controversial methods with which the Michurinites have made us all too familiar in later years.

In 1938, as already mentioned, the Michurinites were strong enough to remove Vavilov from the Presidency of the Academy of Agricultural Sciences, and in 1940 he lost his two important working posts as Director of the Institute of Plant Industry and of the Genetics Institute. He had previously been attacked on the grounds that, when asked whether he could produce certain new and improved crop varieties, he had replied in the affirmative, but with the proviso that it would take at least five years to do so. (Apparently in the U.S.S.R. a reasonable degree of scientific caution can be interpreted as being unpatriotic !). According to Muller, who has been at great pains to discover the facts, in 1940, during the period of the Hitler-Stalin pact, he was accused of being a British spy. It is certain that he was arrested in that year, he was sent to the far north-east of Siberia (probably in 1941), and that he died there in 1942, apparently largely as the result of the hardships he had suffered since 1940.

Sir Henry Dale (1949), who was then President of the Royal Society, tells us that it was only in 1945 that the Society discovered that he had been disgraced and had died. " Repeated enquiries, addressed to the Academy by the Royal Society through all available channels, asking only the date and the place of his death, received no reply of any kind."

That was the miserable end of one of the best scientists that Russia has ever produced.

Meanwhile, in 1943, Lysenko had published a book presenting his considered views on heredity, later (1946) translated into English by Dobzhansky with the title " Heredity and its Variability." The vague and unscientific treatment shocked western scientists ; but the confident way in which he justified his views on ideological grounds indicated the strength of his position in the U.S.S.R. That position was still further strengthened, according to information I have received, by the publication in Britain of Hudson and Richen's careful review of the situation. For they made out that Lysenko, in the later presentations of his theories, was being a strict exponent of dialectical materialism ; whereas some of his opponents in the U.S.S.R. had been claiming that his philosophical standpoint was not wholly orthodox.

When I was in the U.S.S.R. in 1945, the fate of Russian genetics was still in the balance. Even though Lysenko had reached a strong position, research in classical (neo-Mendelian) genetics was still proceeding in various Institutes, and excellent work was still being done in that field (see Huxley, 1945).

As late as 1945–46, as revealed in the meetings of the Academy of Sciences in August, 1948 (reported in *Izvestia* ; and see Nujdin, 3 p. 120), the Academy was considering whether the best way of dealing with the long-drawn out controversy would not be to create a new Institute of the Academy under the neo-Mendelian Dubinin (later disgraced and deprived of his post as a result of the 1948 discussion), to deal with Mendelian genetics, in addition to the old Institute of Genetics, which had come under the control of Lysenko and was working along Michurinist lines.

However, the Michurinites were busy arranging for a final show-down. Late in 1948 (I quote from Muller) " the remaining geneticists, and those biologists in related fields who still had the temerity to support the genetic viewpoint, were caught in a carefully laid trap. They were invited to express their views in the columns of the *Moscow Literary Gazette*. Several of them took advantage of this seeming return to freedom of scientific discussion by restating the case for genetics. Lysenko and Prezent thereupon replied in their characteristic style. The discussion furnished an excuse for a new Soviet ' Conference on genetics.' This, the third " genetics controversy," took the shape of a special session of the Academy of Agricultural Sciences from July 31 to August 7, 1948. The extracts from its proceedings, given in succeeding chapters, show the extraordinary nature of the discussion—the arrogance, the ideological assurance and the unscientific approach of the Michurinites and the apologetic attitude of most of the Mendelians.

Towards its close Lysenko revealed that his views had the approval of the Central Committee of the Communist Party, upon which a sweeping resolution was passed condemning neo-Mendelism and exalting Michurinism. The matter was then considered by the U.S.S.R. Academy of Sciences, the highest and most powerful scientific body in the land, which passed further resolutions in the same sense, and took various steps to implement them.

With this, the genetics controversy was over. Mendelism was proscribed, and Michurinism was installed in the position, unknown in the west, of an official science.

CHAPTER 2

THE IDEOLOGICAL ISSUE

In the preceding chapter, I explained some of the facts
concerning the two rival systems involved in the genetics
controversy in the U.S.S.R., and set forth something of
the history of the dispute, which had its origins 20 years
back or more, and was acute for a period of 12 years
from 1936.

In this chapter, I shall deal with the main issue involved in the controversy. In 1948, the dispute came
to a close—at least for the time being—with the complete defeat of neo-Mendelism and the enthronement of
Michurinism as official doctrine in the sphere of genetics
and evolution. The time has now come for those in
other countries to take stock of the situation and its implications. Scientifically I believe that the situation is
very grave. There is now a party line in genetics, which
means that the basic scientific principle of the appeal to
fact has been overridden by ideological considerations.
A great scientific nation has repudiated certain basic
elements of scientific method, and in so doing has repudiated the universal and supranational character of
science.

That is the major issue. Its discussion has been unfortunately clouded by insistence on subsidiary, minor,
and sometimes irrelevant issues. In relation to this
main issue, it is subsidiary whether or not Lysenko's
claims to have made certain new discoveries are substantiated, and whether his theories are wholly or partly
sound. It leaves the main issue untouched if the at-

tempt is made to justify the action taken, on the narrowly practical ground that the agricultural production of the U.S.S.R. must be rapidly increased, or on the more general ground that Marxism must believe in the improvement of the environment, and must or would like to believe that such improvements have a permanent effect on heredity. It is of no relevance to the main issue that Mendelism has sometimes been used to justify undesirable theories and actions, such as Nazi racialist theories or the exaggerated theories of inherent class superiority put forward by certain eugenists. It is equally irrelevant that Mendel was a Roman Catholic priest, or that this or that noted geneticist was a political reactionary. It is a subsidiary issue that some geneticists in the U.S.S.R. may have been directly or indirectly " liquidated." It is confusing the real issue to recall that in a wholly or partly planned economy the State must decide how money should be spent on scientific research and its application ; or that men of science outside the U.S.S.R. cannot always obtain official grants for the researches they want to undertake, or always get their papers accepted for publication ; or that capitalist as well as communist countries insist on secrecy for certain kinds of research, and deny free publication to their results. All these issues are, I repeat, either irrelevant or merely subsidiary to the major issue, which is the official condemnation of scientific results on other than scientific grounds, and therefore the repudiation by the U.S.S.R. of the concept of scientific method and scientific activity held by the great majority of men of science elsewhere.

To make the issue clear, I will begin by quoting from the report of the proceedings of a meeting of the Praesidium (the usual English term would be *Council* or

perhaps *Executive Committee*) of the U.S.S.R. Academy
of Sciences of August 26, 1948 (I, p. 663), the highest and
most powerful scientific authority in the land, to which
the issue, after previous debates by the Academy of
Agricultural Sciences (see later), was referred. Here
and elsewhere I have italicized passages which seem to
me particularly relevant. When passages are from
verbatim translations, I have given them in double
quotes (" . . . ") ; when from summarized reports, in
single quotes (' . . . ').

. The Praesidium of the Academy of Sciences passed
twelve resolutions. Of these the most important for
our purpose are the following (the translation has been
slightly condensed) :

' (3) The Cytogenetical Laboratory of Cytology,
Histology and Embryology headed by N. P. Dubinin,
shall be abolished *as unscientific and useless*. The
Laboratory of Botanical Cytology at the same institute
shall be closed down *on the grounds that it has followed
the same incorrect and unscientific line* . . . .

'(4) The Bureau of the Division of Biological Sciences
shall be charged with the preparation of plans for
scientific research work for the years 1948–50. *In this
the Bureau shall be guided by Michurin's teaching*, and shall
adjust the scientific research work of biological
institutes to the needs of national economy.

' (6) The composition of Scientists' Councils at
biological institutes and editorial boards of biological
publications shall be checked with the object of remov-
ing from them *the partisans of Morgano-Weismannite
genetics* and of replacing them by *supporters of progressive
Michurinite biology*.

' (7) The Division of History and Philosophy shall be
charged with inclusion in its programme of populariza-

tion of the achievements of Michurinism and of *critical exposure of the pseudo-scientific Morgano-Weismannite tendency.*

' (11) The Bureau of the Division of Biological Sciences shall revise the syllabuses at biological institutes, *bearing in mind the interests of Michurinism.*

An explanatory statement follows, including the following remarks : ' At a number of Academy institutes *formal genetics has not been combated with sufficient vigour.* For this the Praesidium of the Academy takes the blame. The Bureau of the Division of Biological Sciences and its head L. A. Orbeli, the distinguished physiologist [who was released from his duties as Academician-Secretary under Resolution I] have failed to give a correct orientation to the biologists of the Academy '.

' The report by Lysenko (1948 ; and [3]), *which has been approved by the Central Committee of the Communist Party, has exposed the scientific inconsistency of the reactionary idealist theories of the followers of Weismannism*—Schmalhausen, Dubinin, Zhebrak, Navashin and others.'

It is worth noting here the way in which the fact of the Communist Party's approval was first made public. It was announced by Lysenko himself during the session of the Academy of Agricultural Sciences. However, he did not make the announcement in his opening report, but only after the close of discussion, at the beginning of the 10th sitting of the Session, in his Concluding Remarks, which paved the way for the final Resolution passed by the Academy.

Here is what he said : " Comrades, before I pass to my concluding remarks I consider it my duty to make the following statement.

' The question is asked in one of the notes handed to me, What is the attitude of the Central Committee of the Party to my report? I answer, the Central Committee of the Party examined my report and approved it (stormy applause. Ovation. All rise)."

The only explanation of this timing seems to be that it was a tactical move, designed to give the discussion the appearance of being free, when in point of fact the issue had already been decided at a higher (political) level. For it would be, to put it mildly, difficult for any scientist in the U.S.S.R. to oppose a position approved by the Central Committee of the Party.

To revert to the Academy of Sciences, a letter to Comrade Stalin is summarized as follows :

' A pledge is here given by the Praesidium of the U.S.S.R. Academy of Sciences to further Michurin's biology *and to root out unpatriotic, idealist, Weismannite-Morganist ideology* '.

A final statement by the Praesidium (" To the prosperity of our progressive science ") is thus summarized : ' Michurin's materialist direction in biology *is the only acceptable form of science, because it is based on dialectical materialism and on the revolutionary principle of changing Nature for the benefit of the people. Weismannite-Morganist idealist teaching is pseudo-scientific, because it is founded on the notion of the divine origin of the world and assumes eternal and unalterable scientific laws. The struggle between the two ideas has taken the form of the ideological class-struggle between socialism and capitalism on the international scale, and between the majority of Soviet scientists and a few remaining Russian scientists who have retained traces of bourgeois ideology, on a smaller scale. There is no place for compromise. Michurinism and Morgan-Weismann-ism cannot be reconciled.*' (Note here, among much else of interest, the apparent distinction between *Soviet* and *Russian* scientists.)

There are also now available Lysenko's " Report on Soviet Biology " to the session of the Lenin Academy of Agricultural Sciences, July 31–August 7, 1948, together with his concluding speech (Lysenko, 1948 ; and in [3]), two summaries of the subsequent discussion ([1],[2]), and verbatim reports of a few of the speeches ([4])[1].

Since this article was first written, a verbatim English translation of the entire discussion, totalling 631 pages, has been published in Moscow([3]). Neither space nor time has been available for the general use of verbatim extracts from this, but I have satisfied myself as to the general accuracy of the summarized citations that I have given.

These reports, together with the documents already cited, constitute a melancholy landmark in the history of science. They demonstrate that science is no longer regarded in the U.S.S.R. as an international activity of free workers whose prime interest it is to discover new truth and new facts, but as an activity subor-

---

[1] It is to be noted that the summary in *Europe*([2]) is somewhat tendentious, in that it does not merely give complete summaries of all the speeches, but groups them under headings, and only summarizes what it considers relevant to each heading. Thus one of its headings is entitled " La Pratique Mitchourienne " and is editorially introduced as follows : " C'est un véritable bilan de victoires qu'a entendu l'Académie d'Agronomie quand défilèrent les savants et praticiens venus de tous les points de l'immense Union Soviétique pour témoigner des résultats positifs de la pratique mitchourienne." (As later pointed out, many of these successes are in point of fact due to the application of ordinary principles of selection, or to the unconscious ulitization of Mendelian principles). Only the parts of the speeches relevant to the success of Michurinism are summarized : other parts are omitted.

Another section is headed " Caractère Réactionnaire de la Génétique formaliste." The section devoted to the speeches of Zhebrak, Zavadovsky and others who defended neo-Mendelism is headed " la Génétique Formaliste."

It should also be mentioned that Waddington's articles (1948-49) do not discuss what appears to me to be the real or at least the major issue.

dinated to a particular ideology and designed only to secure practical results in the interests of a particular national and political system. Consequently the unity of science is denied, and various brands of " good " science—Marxist, Soviet, or materialist—are distinguished from various brands of " bad " science—bourgeois, reactionary, idealist and the like. Further, the primary sanction for scientific theory is no longer consonance with the facts of nature, but consonance with a political and social philosophy. With this, orthodoxy is once more enthroned ; and though this is no longer the theological orthodoxy from whose bonds the western world emancipated itself in the seventeenth, eighteenth and nineteenth centuries, the new social-political orthodoxy is equally powerful, employs abuse and force in a similar way, and is equally inimical to the free spirit of science. There is now a scientific party line in the U.S.S.R., and those who stray from it do so at their peril.

It is true that up to the present this complete subordination of science to political authority applies only in genetics. However, tendencies in the same direction have also manifested themselves in the U.S.S.R. with more or less force in other fields of creative and intellectual activity—philosophy, literature, the visual arts and even music—and in other scientific subjects, such as psychology and the theory of probability. Further, once the principle of a dominant orthodoxy has been admitted and acted upon on one field, it can readily be generalized, and the presumption is that it will be. In any event, there can now be no security that other branches of science in the U.S.S.R. will not suffer the same fate as genetics, and be *gleichgeschaltet* in relation to an overriding system.

Let me illustrate these points by quotations, at the same time trying to imagine what would have happened if the controversy had developed in Britain or other centre of " bourgeois science."

In the first place, the two sides have been elaborately labelled, and many of the labels have philosophical or political connotations, often implying approval or condemnation. Thus, neo-Mendelism is usually referred to as *Morgano-Mendelism*, often with one or more of the adjectives *formalist, idealist* or *reactionary* prefixed ; or simply as *idealist genetics*. Sometimes it is styled ' Weismannism ' (again usually with a pejorative prefix), although in the west, Weismann's particular views are now mainly of historical interest only. We are told that the views of the neo-Mendelians are *mystic, metaphysical, bourgeois, pseudo-scientific*, or even *anti-scientific*.

The followers of Lysenko, on the other hand, are called *Michurinites*, presumably because the Soviet tendency is to justify the present in terms of past authority, and Michurin is being deliberately glorified as a great Russian pioneer in agricultural and biological science (whereas in point of fact he was essentially an empiricist who scored some important practical successes, but whose theoretical speculations have become scientifically negligible in the light of later research). Timiriazev is also often cited as an authority under whose banner Lysenko and his followers are advancing (although his genetical theories are now quite outdated by scientific advance). Further, Michurinism is usually qualified with the adjective *scientific, materialist,* or *progressive*. The term *Soviet genetics* is not infrequently used, and Lysenko employs the phrase *Soviet creative Darwinism*.

Subtletly of description is pushed to extremes by
B. M. Zavadovsky, who distinguishes between *Mendelism*
as a system of established facts, and *Mendelianism* as
Mendelism distorted by reactionary idealist and metaphysical elements. (But Zavadovsky was in a very
awkward position, as an ardent and important member
of the Communist Party who had for several decades
done a great deal to popularize neo-Mendelism.)

In Britain or the U.S.A., I suppose we should have
heard simply of certain new claims of Lysenko which
required confirmation, and of certain new theories of his
which were in conflict with accepted views ; or perhaps
the matter would have developed into a general dispute
between neo-Mendelians and Michurinites, in the same
way that the quarrel between Karl Pearson and Bateson
developed into a general dispute between biometricians
and Mendelians some 40 odd years ago. Individual
participants in the controversy might have been
stigmatized as old-fashioned or uncritical ; but there
would certainly have been no wholesale attaching of
philosophical, political or moral labels.

In the second place, the two chief touchstones in the
controversy in the U.S.S.R. have been, not scientific fact
and verification of theory by experiment, but immediate
practical utility on one hand and correctness of doctrine
on the other. The criterion of practical utility is
probably of less general significance. In any event, it
is not universally applied. I can testify from personal
experience at the time of the celebrations of the Academy
of Sciences in 1945, that there was in many fields,
including ecology, genetics, systematics and general
biology as a whole, an admirable balance between
' pure ' and ' applied ' work in the U.S.S.R., and that
some branches of science with negligible practical

applications, such as vertebrate paleontology, were extremely flourishing (see Huxley, 1945). However, in the case of genetics, the utilitarian criterion has been drastically employed—largely, I imagine, because the controversy has been so largely guided by Lysenko, and Lysenko is an agriculturist whose primary aim has been to achieve success through spectacular practical results.

Thus, in his " Report " Lysenko (1948) says : " Socialist Agriculture, the collective and state farming system, has given rise to a Soviet biological science, founded by Michurin—a science *new in principle* [italics mine throughout, unless otherwise stated], developing in close union with agronomical practice. . . . It is no exaggeration to say that *Morgan's feeble metaphysical ' science '* . . . can stand no comparison with our *effective Michurinist agrobiological science.*"

Lysenko later refers to Michurin as " the great transformer of Nature", and says " in our country the Morganist cytogeneticists find themselves confronted by the *practical effectiveness of the Michurin trend* in agrobiological science." With reference to the special laboratory under Zhebrak, set up in the Timiriazev Academy by the Ministry of Agriculture, to study chromosome doubling (polyploidy)[1] in plants (which, I may mention, has obtained some extremely interesting results), Lysenko merely says that, in his view, " it has produced literally nothing of practical value. Here is one example, . . . to show how useless is the practical and theoretical programme of our domestic Morganist cytogeneticists." Finally, in the conclusion of his " Report," he writes that " *a scientific handling of practical problems is the surest way to a deeper knowledge of the laws of development of living nature* (italics his)—a

---

[1] Reduplication of entire sets of chromosomes : see Chap. 4.

sweeping assertion in obvious contradiction with many events in the history of science.

In the discussion, the same thesis is reiterated. Thus Nemchinov states that the task of agricultural science is to change nature for the benefit of socialist economy (*nota bene*, not of humanity in general), and Lobanov says that Soviet agricultural science must ' aim at the successful solution of practical problems ' (a statement with which no one would quarrel if it were not constantly extended to mean that all genetics must be directed *only* to the solution of practical problems). Some of the speakers went even further. Olshansky says that Morgano-Mendelism ' *obstructs* the work of practical breeding and seed-growing.' Turbin ([3], p. 479) says that the discoveries of Michurin genetics " proved that the explanation of heredity given by the chromosome theory is useless." He apparently is not concerned whether it is *true ;* and Babajanyan ([3], p. 163) makes the following extraordinary statement " *By its very nature your theory* [Mendelism-Morganism] *is directed* against practice . . . We must say very emphatically that the Mendelist-Morganist theory is *inimical to practice* . . . The Mendelists are not only enemies of established and proved achievements, but also potential enemies of all future achievements. (Applause)." Dubinin's interesting study of the selective effect of environment on the genetic composition of a population of *Drosophila*, because it is of no immediate practical value, is described by Yakushkin as ' *a monstrous deviation from the tasks of a Soviet scientist*,' and its author was called " unpatriotic " by Mitin. Lysenko, in his Report, held it up to ridicule, in a way quite unworthy of a scientific discussion. Yet this was part of the work which so recently as 1947, in his book

" Science Advances," Professor J. B. S. Haldane (who is a good communist and also a good geneticist) described as having " led to new perspectives both of evolution and of human congenital disease."

Babajanyan, when asked by Rapoport why he shut his eyes to the existence of useful as opposed to deleterious mutations in *Drosophila*, answered ([3] ; p. 163) " *because they are useful mutations for a useless object.*" Previously he had said " Who wants what by their very nature are useless *Drosophilas* ? " There could not be a clearer repudiation of the idea that one of the basic functions of science is to obtain knowledge and understanding.

Dimitriev condemns all scientific work (in genetics) which does not assist practical agriculture, and criticizes Schmalhausen and others '*for expressing views incompatible with progressive improvement in agriculture.*' (Apparently, he regards it as irrelevant whether the views happen to be true or not.)

On the other hand, some speakers give the practical criterion a twist and assert that ' Morgano-Mendelism is a bourgeois philosophy *seeking nothing but the exploitation of Nature* ' (Dvorjankin), and that ' self-pollination and selection of selfed lines of maize use Morganist techniques, which made seed-production difficult *and play into the hands of capitalist seed-firms* ' (Feiginson).

One of the reasons given by the Academy for closing down the Cytogenetical Laboratory under Dubinin (see above) is that it is " useless." (The Academy must have forgotten Faraday's answer to a questioner who asked him what was the use of his work : " What is the use of a baby ? ")

In Britain, the practical utility of this or that discovery or the immediate applicability of this or that theory would doubtless have been discussed ; but no one would have questioned the desirability of leaving a considerable free sector to pure research, whether on the two-fold ground, usually accepted here, that one of the aims of science is to increase knowledge irrespective of practical results, and that practical results do, as a matter of fact, often spring from what appear to be the most impractical investigations, or, in the case of a minority, for the latter reason only. More Government money might have gone into Michurinite work if the Government and its advisers had been impressed by Lysenko's claims ; but it is safe to say that no laboratory turning out a considerable volume of research results would have been closed down as useless.

More central to the issue is the appeal to doctrine and authority instead of to observational and experimental verification. As a result, a basic effect of the controversy has been to establish, in the fields of genetics and evolution, a scientific orthodoxy, which in its turn is related to and dependent upon a philosophical orthodoxy. And the philosophical orthodoxy is, of course, linked with the social and political orthodoxy of Communism and the authority of the Communist Party in the U.S.S.R. The upshot is that science in U.S.S.R. must now do its work in a totally different atmosphere and on totally different intellectual foundations from those in other countries.

The full extent of the change of attitude and atmosphere can only be properly appreciated by reading the actual proceedings of the session in detail. However, I will try to convey its essence by some extracts.

In the first place there is often a stress on the truth or falsity of " teaching " (" doctrine," " standpoint," or

47

" trend ") which recalls scholasticism rather than science[1]. Thus Perov says " *the only true trend* in the science of biology is the Michurin trend." Nuzhdin gives three examples ' *supporting Michurin's teaching.*' Lysenko himself in his " Report " writes : " The appearance of Darwin's *teaching*, expounded in his book ' The Origins of Species,' marked the beginning of scientific biology. The primary idea in Darwin's theory is his *teaching* on natural and artificial selection." Lysenko himself in his concluding remarks[3] writes : ". . . for the first time in the history of biology(!) *a truly effective theory* (in French[2] *une veritable theorie scientifique*) has come into being—*the Michurin teaching.*" Prezent[3] says " in order that the Morganists might be 'reconciled' with the Michurinian theory, *they would have to renounce every one of the theoretical concepts of their false doctrine.*"

Finally, the resolution adopted at the session sums up the issue by saying : " L'Académie Lénine des Sciences Agronomiques doit devenir réellement un

---

[1] It is difficult to disentangle the various terms, since in different translations or summaries the same Russian words may be translated differently. However, two conclusions are quite clear. First, that the Michurinites equate the terms *theory* and *teaching* (see Lysenko's remarks, below) ; so that for them a scientific theory means something quite different from what it does to western scientists, who regard it as a general framework of concepts giving a satisfactory interpretation of a mass of established facts and laws ; and secondly that the various terms such as *teaching*, *trend*, *doctrine* and *theory* mean some body of ideas whose truth or falsity can be determined *a priori*, or at least on ideological grounds, rather than by testing against the facts of nature.

Truth, like other general terms, can be employed in various senses. For western scientists, " scientific truth " has to do with a process— the slow accumulation of tested facts and the growth of explanatory ideas providing insight and understanding of nature. For Soviet scientists, it is clearly something more, since it is concerned with the underlying assumptions which science ought to make in relation to a dominant general ideology. One is tempted to add that it is more scholastic, and indeed metaphysical, although both these terms are applied abusively by the Michurinites to the views of their opponents.

centre scientifigue *pour l'élaboration approfondie de la doctrine Michourienne* "[2].

The manifesto referred to on p. 662 of the summary in *Plant Breeding Abstracts*([1]), under the title of " Up the Flag of Progressive Michurinite Biological Science," goes further, in stating that Lysenko's " Report " ' *shows* that *Michurin's teaching is materialist and progressive,* while *the teaching of Weismann, Mendel and Morgan is reactionary and idealist.*' Here, as in Perov's earlier cited remarks, we have the distinction between true and false doctrines or trends, a distinction occasionally over-emphasized by zealots, such as Belenky, who describes Darwin and Lamarck as *infallible* (in spite of Lysenko himself having pointed out numerous " errors " in Darwin's " teaching ").

The truth or falsity of doctrine is, as already indicated, linked up with the relation of scientific theories to politico-philosophical orthodoxy. This theme recurs constantly throughout the controversy. Lobanov says that ' Morgano-Mendelism is *a bourgeois philosophy.*' Dvorjankin goes the whole hog, in throwing doubt even on the facts discovered by the upholders of false doctrine, for he says that ' *too much credence should not be given to bourgeois science.*' Alikhanyan, one of the few practising Mendelians who spoke, while insisting that ' there is nothing idealist about chromosomes and genes ', endeavours to show his conformity with doctrinal orthodoxy by adding that ' *they must be considered in the light of dialectical materialism, and the chromosome theory must be purged of idealist elements.*'

As a corollary of all this, any defence of neo-Mendelism immediately becomes "propaganda" for the " false doctrine." Thus Kostryukova complains that Russian biological journals such as the *Journal of General*

Biology or the *Comptes Rendus* (*Doklady*, *Reports*) *of the U.S.S.R. Academy of Sciences* have for some years published ' no articles with a Michurinite tendency.' Thus, ' thanks to this choice of articles, *Morganist propaganda* was being conducted in every part of our country. However, in future, as we have seen, *the editors of scientific journals are no longer to have the right to select what articles they think are scientifically valuable.*' That this is now the case is confirmed by the Minister of Higher Education himself (Kaftanov, 1948), who after referring to " the reactionary Weismann-Morgan theories," states that " our present aim is to fill the ranks of the teaching profession with Michurinist biologists."

Perov says that ' present [Russian] textbooks on genetics are full of *formal and unscientific nonsense.* Glushchenko, Lysenko's chief helper, deduces the inheritance of acquired characters, not from experiment but from first principles, in a manner reminiscent of scholastic theology : ' *Dialectics . . . show* that biological processes involve the principle of external action, and *that such external influences become internal properties after assimilation by the organism.*' The seventh resolution of the Praesidium of the U.S.S.R. Academy of Sciences charges the Division of History and Philosophy with " the critical exposure of *the pseudo-scientific Morgano-Weismannist teaching.*"

Lysenko in his " Report " says that a major error of Darwin lay in his " transferring into his *teaching Malthus' preposterous reactionary ideas* on population," (a statement which readers of Darwin's *Autobiography* will recognise as so distorted as to be quite false). Later he writes " Reactionary biologists everywhere have . . . done everything in their power to empty

Darwinsim of its materialist elements "—a somewhat strange accusation to bring against the neo-Mendelians who have discovered and elucidated the material basis of heredity in the chromosomes, and in so doing appear to be on the track of the essential material basis of life itself.

This is a very sore spot with the Michurinites. Thus when Nemchinov was saying that he could not agree that " the chromosomes have no relations with the mechanism of heredity," there was a disturbance in the hall, and one delegate shouted " There are no such mechanisms." Perov ([3]; p. 146) speaks of the " mystical, mythical, and actually non-material (!) gene." Prezent, the philosophic interpreter of Lysenko, says that " nobody will be led astray by the Morganists' false analogies concerning the invisible atom and the invisible gene. *Far closer would be an analogy between the invisible gene and the invisible spirit.*" It seems incredible that a man who claims to be a philosopher could descend to such " arguments." It can only be because he has no serious arguments to put forward. In any case the facts are against him. The existence of genes and of atoms has been demonstrated in an essentially similar way, the spatial arrangement of genes within chromosomes can be ascertained with an exactitude as great as that of atoms within molecules ; they have been seen under the electron microscope ; and their chemical make-up is beginning to be known. Turbin ([2]; p. 141; translated rather differently in [3]) reveals his biological ignorance (or unwillingness to consider facts) in his conclusion : ' We reject the fantastic assertion of the Morgano-Mendelists, according to which, to deny the genes would be to deny the material basis of the phenomena of heredity.' On the contrary, he continues, it is the cell which must be ' considered as the material basis of the phenomena of heredity '—which is, of course, in a sense true, but so vague as to put biology back by 80 years.

Lysenko in his " Report " writes as follows : "Again, an example of how uncritically our Mendelist-Morganists accept *idealistic genetics* is the fact that the standard textbook on genetics in many of our colleges has until quite recently been a translated American textbook, by Sinnott and Dunn " (which if not perfect, is certainly both competent and comprehensive). He even goes so far as to describe Morganism as a " *pseudo-science*."

In order to support his own Lamarckian or what one might call Michurino-Lamarckian views, Lysenko frequently states that the inheritance of acquired characters is *materialist*, whereas Weismannism and Mendelo-Morganism are *idealist, mystical, formalist, scholastic* and *metaphysical*. He even claims that " *the materialist theory of the evolution of living nature . . . is unthinkable without recognition of the inheritance of acquired characters*." In the 1939 discussion on genetics, Lysenko made the following statements : " When he grasps Bolshevism, the reader will not be able to give his sympathy to metaphysics, and *Mendelism definitely is pure, undisguised metaphysics*." ([5] ; p. 155). " *It is possible to defend the false bases of Mendelism only by lies* . . . The teaching of Mendel and Morgan I cannot call anything but false." ([5] ; p. 154).

He asks for the complete exposure of the " Morganist metaphysics, which is in its entirety an importation from *foreign reactionary biology hostile to us*." Here we have the logical extreme of the subordination of scientific theory to a socio-political philosophy, in the shape of its subordination to nationalism. It becomes unpatriotic to believe in neo-Mendelian facts, because Mendelism is a product of scientists from bourgeois and capitalist countries. Thus Lysenko later says that in the U.S.S.R. " young scientists with an insight into questions of philosophy have in recent years come to realize that the *Morganist views are utterly alien to the world outlook of Soviet people* "—as if this, and not their concordance with the facts of Nature, were the criterion of their scientific validity !

Mitin is summarized thus : ' *the reactionary, idealist Morgano-Mendelian* school of thought . . . is condemned, and its followers are called *unpatriotic*.' Zhebrak, who had the temerity to publish an article in *Science*, criticizing Lysenko and his methods, was publicly criticized by the Timiriazev Academy for his " unpatriotic action " ; and Nuzhdin says that Zhebrak's article showed that the neo-Mendelians in the U.S.S.R. were " ready to form a common front with the most reactionary bourgeois genetics." Prezent[3] refers to " *the corrupting influence of Morganism* " as having penetrated into non-biological circles in the U.S.S.R. He also says ([3] ; p. 598) " Morganism is having a pernicious effect on some of our philosophers, *whose duty it is to have a correct point of view concerning the ideological significance inherent in questions of biology*."

Plesetsky ([3] ; p. 106) " The war had not ended when the fomenters of a new imperialist war appeared on the political scene in the capitalist countries . . . Among them were Sax, Darlington and other representatives of Mendelism-Morganism." Even apart from the fact that neither Sax in the U.S.A. nor Darlington in Britain have played any political role, this could hardly justify the rejection of neo-Mendelism as a science, as he urges.

Unworthy motives are ascribed to foreign men of

science. Thus Prezent, the philosophical *éminence grise* of Lysenko, referring to the painstakingly fair and almost ultra-conscientious appraisal of the work of Lysenko and his school by the two Englishmen, Hudson and Richens (1946), does not scruple to say that ' *the motives of Hudson and Richens*, who suggest that Russian varieties may not be pure, *are . . . questioned.*'

Finally, the Praesidium of the U.S.S.R. Academy of Sciences itself, in a letter to Stalin([2]), pledges itself ' to root out *unpatriotic, idealist Weismannite-Morganist ideology.*'

This preoccupation with teaching or doctrine and with an overriding philosophy leads logically on to two further results—the establishment of a party line in science, and the division of science into two camps. Thus the manifesto from which I have previously quoted ([1] : p. 662) also states that ' the Report by Lysenko, which has been approved by the Central Committee of the All-Union Communist Party (Bolsheviks), *lays down the party line in biology.*' Zhebrak, in a letter (summarized in [1] ; p. 662), writes that he " finds it necessary to withdraw from his previous position [on genetics], *since this has been declared mistaken by the Central Committee of the All-Union Communist Party.*"

The question of the unity of science clearly pre-occupies the more philosophically minded Michurinites ; but their claim that scientific work in a capitalist country must be tainted with bourgeois ideology, and to such an extent that its scientific value may be thereby vitiated, enables them to deal with it to their own satisfaction.

Listen once more to Prezent ([2]; p. 134; my translation from French)[1] : ' The opponents of the Mich-

---

[1] This apparently verbatim French translation frequently differs from the official English translation in ([3]) ; presumably it is a summary.

urinite trend to agrobiology and their allies have invited us to recognize the rational elements in *bourgeois biological science* and not to break our links with *so-called world science*. It is true that we Michurinites *do not have the same conception as the Morganists as to what classical biological science has bequeathed to us, nor as to what the Morganists call " contemporary world biological science." The content they give to this term is territorial, not theoretical. World biological science is represented by the most progressive science* [la science d'avant-garde] *at each stage of its history. To-day, the most progressive materialist biological science is the Michurinite tendency of Soviet agrobiology. ' Is it not extraordinary that in our country,* where dialectical materialism is the methodological basis of science, with an undeniably revolutionary character, *there appear from time to time dreams of the unity of our science with contemporary foreign science ? '*

This at least is plain : we know now that the U.S.S.R. does not believe in the unity of science. But it is worth recalling that " world science " in any branch is represented not merely by its actual *avant-garde* tendencies, but also by the body of knowledge accumulated by past generations of scientific workers.

And Prezent ([2] ; p. 137) makes himself still clearer when he is treating of free scientific discussion. ' Nobody forbids and nobody can forbid discussion in science. Let us accordingly discuss *within the frame-work* [à l'intérieur même] *of the Michurinite tendency,* the best way of studying this doctrine, and applying it in practice. *But it is high time to demand from you your participation in the struggle against the theories of foreign biologists.'* (The translation in [3], p. 602 runs : The Morganists " want a discussion. *But we shall not discuss with the Morganists* (applause) ; *we shall continue to expose them* as adherents of an essentially false scientific trend, *a pernicious and ideologically alien trend, brought to our country from foreign shores.* (Applause)." Here we have it in black and white. Free discussion—but within limits. No freedom for " foreign " theories except to be combated).

During the actual session, a few Mendelians were allowed to defend their views. Nemchinov and Rapoport came out openly in opposition to Lysenko, and various others such as Alikhanyan and B. M. Zavadovsky defended the general validity of neo-Mendelian genetics. But the general atmosphere was extremely hostile to them, and almost all were apologetic or tried to justify their views on the basis of Marxist principles. There had clearly been a marked tightening-up since the earlier pre-war congresses on genetics, when many more Mendelians spoke, and spoke much more freely (Muller, 1948 ; and see [5]).

Of course, when Lysenko announced that his views had the official approval of the Communist Party ([3] ; p. 605), it was clear that the Mendelians were being allowed to speak merely to give a semblance of free discussion (as well, perhaps, as to give them a rope to hang themselves with). They have now all been dismissed or disgraced. Further, from now on (until official policy changes) there can be no further freedom of speech on genetics ; neo-Mendelism is to be denounced and combated, not discussed.

Lysenko's " Concluding Remarks " drew to their close. " The present session," he said " has demonstrated *the complete triumph of the Michurin trend over Mendelism-Morganism* (applause).

" Progressive biological science owes it to the geniuses of mankind, *Lenin* and *Stalin*, that *the teaching of I. V.*

Michurin has been added to the treasure house of our knowledge, has become part of the gold fund of our science. (Applause).

" Long live the Michurin teaching, which shows how to transform living nature for the benefit of the Soviet people ! (*Applause*).

" Long live the Party of Lenin and Stalin, which discovered Michurin for the world (*applause*) and created all the conditions for the progress of advanced materialist biology in our country (*applause*).

Glory to the great friend and protagonist of science, our leader and teacher, Comrade Stalin ! (*All rise. Prolonged applause*) " [1]

The Chairman then announced that three of the speakers in the discussion desired to make a statement. They were Zhukovsky, who had strongly supported Mendelism and the chromosome-theory, and had challenged some of the Michurinites' claims ; Alikhanyan, a younger man, who had wanted to keep the chromosome-theory, while " purging it of idealist elements " ; and Polyakov, who also had wanted a reconciliation between Mendelism and Michurinism, had defended Schmalhausen, and had pointed out certain fallacies in Lamarckism.

Their " statements " ([3] ; p. 618, *ff*) were recantations of past errors and promises of future amendment. Zhukovsky said " The speech I made the day before yesterday, at a time when the Central Committee of the Communist Party had drawn a dividing line between the two trends in biological science [2], was unworthy of a member of the Communist Party and of a Soviet scientist." However, " it was my last speech

[1] ([3] ; p. 617 ; italics in original).

[2] Although he could not know then that it had done so, as the fact was only announced by Lysenko after the close of the discussion.

57

from an incorrect biological and ideological standpoint."

"Academician Vasilenko's speech. . . made a deep impression upon me, for he showed how closely the Michurinites are connected with the people, and how important it is at this juncture to cherish the prestige of our President " (i.e. Lysenko) . . .

" I declare I shall fight—and there are times when I can fight—for the Michurinian biological science (*Prolonged applause*)."

" I am a man of responsibility . . . I therefore consider that it is my moral duty to be a sincere Michurinist and sincere Soviet biologist " . . .

" Believe me, that I take this step to-day as a Party member . . . "

The subordination of science to the Party line could not well be more clearly expressed.

Alikhanyan ascribed his errors to the influence of his teachers. But now " it is important to realize that we must be on this side of the scientific barricades, with our Party and with our Soviet science " . . .

" It would be foolish to think that we are being asked to discard everything good and useful accumulated in the development of science. What we are being asked to do is to discard everything reactionary, false and useless " . . .

" I, as a Communist, cannot and must not, in the ardour of controversy, obstinately oppose my personal views and concepts to the onward march of biological science " . . .

" From to-morrow on I shall not only myself, in all my scientific activity, try to emancipate myself from the old reactionary Weismann-Morganian views, but shall try to reform and convince all my pupils and comrades". . . .

" Only in our country, the country with the most advanced and progressive world outlook, can the seedlings of the new scientific trend develop " . . .

Here, besides conformity to the Party line, we find the idea that there is an irreconcilable struggle between bourgeois and Soviet science, in which it is a patriotic duty to take part.

Polyakov, while still standing for some freedom of scientific discussion, has also realized that " the Michurinian trend . . . is the only possible road for Bolsheviks, Party and non-Party, who desire to work in the field of our biological science " . . .

" One must be logical and not try to reconcile irreconcilables " . . .

" For the scientist who takes his science seriously and loves it, to change front in short order is hardly a seemly thing . . . But it is necessary to understand the chief and fundamental thing, namely that our Party has helped us to effect a profound and radical reconstruction of our science, has shown us that the Michurinian trend defines the basic line of development of Soviet biological science " . . .

" We must assist our Party in expressing the reactionary pseudo-scientific rot which is disseminated by our enemies abroad " . . .

" The Michurinian trend of science, headed by T. D. Lysenko, is a profoundly scientific popular movement . . . It is in this trend that I too will work, devoting all my strength to the promotion of the great Michurinian theory."

For some reason, Polyakov's recantation was not greeted with applause. However, it demonstrates once more that Soviet scientists recognize the right of the Communist Party to decide what science is right and what wrong, (or, since here might is right, they recognize the need of conforming to its decisions). It is also interesting in its praise of Michurinism as a " popular movement." We shall meet with this criterion again in relation to the controversy over Soviet music (Chapter 5).

We must also mention the personal letter of retraction which Yuri Zdanov wrote to Stalin, and which was published in *Pravda*. Yuri Zhdanov's opinions are of some importance, as he is the son of the celebrated A. A. Zhdanov, who played the leading role in the consolidation of Soviet thought and culture after the war (see Chapter 5). In this letter (I quote the summary given by Langdon-Davies, 1949), " he retracts four errors perpetrated by himself : (1) He had spoken on the genetic controversy as an individual rather than a member of the Communist Party. (2) He had tried to find points of agreement between Michurinism and formal genetics instead of expressing their incompatibility. (3) He had criticized Lysenko, to the delight [and benefit] of the anti-Michurinists. (4) He had treated Weismannism objectively instead of inveighing against its errors."

Since writing the above, I have been able to obtain a verbatim translation of the letter. Since the letter is of great interest, and appears not to be available elsewhere, I have reproduced it in a Postscript.

If the discussion had taken place in Britain or the U.S.A., I do not think that there would have been any of these rather humiliating recantations, nor would either philosophical, political or patriotic labels have been attached to the contending parties, except perhaps on a very limited scale, and certainly without the strong connotations of praise and blame—and of official

praise and blame, involving serious practical consequences—which are found in the U.S.S.R. Some of
the labels, if attached at all, would probably have been
attached the other way round ; thus any speaker who
supported one view on the ground that it emanated
from British or American sources, or attacked the
opposite view because it was foreign, would probably
have been criticized for introducing nationalism into
science.

In any event, participants in such a discussion in the
English-speaking world would certainly not seek
support for their views from authority, or from any
particular philosophy or party, and it is inconceivable
that the discussion should have ended in the laying
down of an official line in science, with the corollary
that certain scientific views should be officially combated. The most that could happen as the direct or
indirect result of such a discussion would be that the
extent of Government support for one line of research
would be increased, for another diminished.

The main issue is now, I hope, clear. It is that in the
U.S.S.R. the scientists who hold certain scientific views
can be called names implying that they are unpatriotic
or hostile to the political system, that scientific theories
can be branded as false and entire branches of science
rejected on ideological grounds, and that accordingly
science, which we used to imagine was the most
universal and international of human activities, has
been split in two.[1]

---

[1] The views of Prof. J. B. S. Haldane and Prof. J. D. Bernal, which
were published too late for me to comment on them in the text, are
referred to in the Postscript (p. 225).

CHAPTER 3

THE SCIENTIFIC ISSUE

I HOPE I have made clear, the scientific aspects of the controversy are subsidiary to the major issue of the freedom and unity of science. Even if Lysenko were right in his claims to have made new and startling genetical discoveries, this could not justify the official condemnation of Mendelism as scientifically false nor the suppression of all Mendelian research. The scientific issues however are of great importance. The issue to be discussed in this chapter is a two-fold one—whether (or how far) Lysenko is scientifically right ; and whether (or how far) neo-Mendelism is scientifically wrong. The word *scientifically* is important. We are not concerned with the question of whether Lysenko's ideas are philosophically sound from the standpoint of Marxist orthodoxy, or whether they are politically expedient, or whether neo-Mendelism is in any way repugnant to Communist ideology, or whether it has been too little concerned with practical applications : we are concerned with the scientific correctness or otherwise of the two rival systems.

This is partly a question of fact—do the chromosomes constitute a physical basis for heredity ? Does grafting affect the hereditary constitution ? And so forth. But it is partly a question of the consonance of any new ideas with what has already been scientifically established. For instance, Lysenko does not merely claim to have obtained certain factual results ; he claims that the Michurinite theory (or as he himself calls it, *doctrine*) of heredity is of general validity. That being so, we have every right to ask how it can interpret established facts, such as Mendelian segregation and recombination, sex-determination and sex-linked inheritance, or the results of natural or artificial chromosome-doubling (polyploidy).

And it is also partly a question of method. Do Lysenko and Muller, for instance, both conduct their experiments with adequate scientific precautions, do they publish their data in such a way that they can be checked by repeating the experiments if so desired, or that they and their implications can be fully grasped by other scientists who read about them ? If not, we can only suspend our scientific judgment on the rightness or wrongness of their claims.

There is undoubtedly a widespread failure to understand scientific method and the distinctive character of science as a human activity, and this on the part of highly-placed administrators and people eminent in their own walks of life, as well as of the general public. In a later chapter, I shall discuss in detail some actual examples of this misapprehension, sometimes amounting to downright ignorance, which have appeared in relation to the Lysenko controversy. But on reflection I felt that it was necessary to do more than this. Accordingly I have tried to explain what is meant by science and scientific method by illustrating it concretely from the actual state and development of genetics. This I shall deal with in the next chapter, under the title " Genetics as a science."

In the present chapter I shall treat of more specific issues. In addition to the general idea of scientific law held in the U.S.S.R., five particular points call for comment. First, the attitude and methods of Lysenko and his followers. Secondly, the two new scientific results claimed by Lysenko and his followers—the claim to have induced the inheritance of acquired characters in plants through partial vernalization, and the claim to have altered their genetic constitution through grafting with other varieties or species. Thirdly, the repudiation of the theory of probability in general, and especially as applied in neo-Mendelian genetics and neo-Darwinian evolution. Fourthly, the repudiation of the whole edifice of neo-Mendelian genetics itself. *Per contra*, and fifthly, the adducing, in support of Michurinism or Lysenkoism, of results which appear more readily (or solely) explicable in terms of neo-Mendelism.

Let me take these in order. First of all, the Michurinites' attitude can only be termed unscientific. In their work, they do not normally employ scientific controls, statistical tests, or the usual scientific precautions such as concern for purity of material ; they seem never to test the validity of alternative explanations ; [1] and their publication of methods and data is frequently quite inadequate to permit either repetition of the work or proper evaluation of the results claimed.

Ashby, who has read all the published material on the experiments of the Lysenko school on the inheritance of the effects of treatment such as partial vernalization and on vegetative hybridization (see below), and is

[1] As an example of faulty methodology, imposed by ideas which take no account of established scientific facts, I may cite the use of mixed pollen from several strains in effecting artificial pollination of experimental plants. This was recommended by Michurin, and is frequently employed by Lysenko and his followers, although any competent botanist knows that this must introduce unpredictable factors into the experiment. Lysenko justifies this on the basis of some wholly speculative ideas about the ova selecting the " best " pollen grains with which to unite. His colleague Prezent even went so far as to coin the term " love-marriage " for this alleged process, which has no foundation in observed fact.

himself a distinguished experimental botanist, writes (1946, p. 261) " The reader cannot judge for himself whether Lysenko has firmly established Michurinian genetics, because the published papers contain very few data. There is no record of a single statistically valid experiment. There is complete absence of suitable controls. And many of the papers draw the most revolutionary conclusions from a solitary experiment."

The Michurinites repeatedly make incorrect statements of fact. Teterev ([3]; p. 402) speaks of the attempts of Darlington and Lawrence to double the number of chromosomes with colchicine, etc. Dr. Darlington tells me that neither he nor Lawrence have ever done any work in this field. This is a small point, though the inaccuracy is symptomatic. But what are we to think of the statement by Plesetsky ([3]; p. 109–110), who says that nectarine-like fruits were produced by some of the seeds from a peach scion grafted onto an apricot stock, that this was due to the grafting, and that it helps to explain the origin of the nectarine. As Crane (1949 b) points out, nectarines are frequently produced by peaches, sometimes from seed, sometimes on individual branches of a growing tree. Darwin in his *Animals and Plants Under Domestication* (1868) cites many examples, including one from the year 1741. Nearly 30 years ago, Connors (1922), showed that the nectarine character of the fruit is a simple recessive to the peach character. Accordingly the production of nectarines from seed is due to ordinary Mendelian segregation, and their production from part of a growing tree is due to the phenomenon, well-known in plants, of somatic mutation. Only ignorance of the subject could excuse the suggestion that grafting had anything to do with the production of nectarines ; but ignorance is itself not excusable in scientific work.

Similar igorance is exhibited by Ushakova ([3] ; p. 199) who, apropos of an erect form of tomato, says " Were there such forms before ? No, there were no such forms." However, as Crane (*loc. cit.*) points out, they have long been known, having been introduced by Vilmorin of Paris in 1860, under the name of *Tree*.

Prezent ([3] ; p. 581) asserts that the appearance of a fruit which had one part red and the rest green, among the offspring of a cross between a red-fruited and a green-fruited strain of apples, is in itself a refutation of Mendelism. It seems impossible to believe that he should not know that similar phenomena are widespread and have been fully explained as due to somatic mutation and the formation of chimaeras, and have no relevance to Mendelian segregation and recombination. But if he did know the facts, he deliberately ignored them ; and ignoring facts is a worse scientific crime than ignorance.

Prezent also refers ([3] ; p. 585) to the fact that Reinette-Bergamotte apples have pear-shaped fruits, and claims as an " incontestable fact " that this was due to vegetative hybridization resulting from a graft made by Michurin between an apple scion and a pear stock. However, as Crane (*loc cit.*) points out, both apple-shaped pears and pear-shaped apples have long been known (the latter were mentioned by Vavilov in one of his more important publications) ; and until the grafting experiment has been repeated with all due precautions, the suggestion that pear-shaped fruits in the Reinette-Bergamotte owe their origin to vegetative hybridization remains unproved and indeed contestable; on the basis of known facts, it is more likely that the character was already present in the strain of apples used as scions.

I could multiply examples, but these must suffice.

They do not carry on discussion in a scientific manner. I have already given some examples of this in the preceding chapter, and though I would have liked to substantiate this too by further citations, I have space but for one ([3] p. 558). Professor Nemchinov, the director of the Timiriazev Academy of Agriculture, was speaking:—" I do not go so far as to share the views of the comrades who assert that chromosomes have nothing to do with the mechanism of heredity." (*Commotion.*)

A voice: " There are no mechanisms " . . .

Nemchinov: ". . . I would not consider it right of A. R. Zhebrak, who committed an anti-patriotic act [in writing a letter to the American journal *Science*, in which he criticized Lysenko] . . . I do not consider that it is necessary because of this to close down his work on amplidiploidy [doubling of chromosome-number in plants, with associated change of properties].

A voice: "You ought to resign."

This is certainly not the way in which a scientific discussion would be carried on in the Royal Society or the National Academy of Sciences.

For further examples, I must refer my readers to the verbatim report of the discussion ([3]).

They neither demand nor accept the same kind of evidence as professional scientists elsewhere ; they confuse fact with doctrine and theory with hypothesis or with belief ; they misuse or redefine terms to suit themselves ; they appeal to past authority instead of to present established fact and to utility instead of truth ; they accept other than scientific criteria, or even insist upon them, in what purports to be a scientific argument. In brief, as Ashby and I found in conversation with Lysenko, they simply do not talk the same language as western scientists.

In general, they betray a lack of appreciation of the special character, validity, and significance of the scientific method as developed in the last few hundred years. I commend the verbatim report to all those concerned for the future of science, although I fear they will find it very depressing reading.

I now pass to the second point, which concerns the claims of the Michurinites to have established new and startling genetic facts. These have been discussed by various general biologists, not specialists in these aspects of genetics, e.g. at length by Hudson and Richens (1946), and more popularly by Waddington (1948–49). More relevant comments come from experts who have themselves worked on the same problems, such as Crane (1949), Darlington (1947), Ashby (1946), etc. Ashby had the rare opportunity of seeing Lysenko's experiments in progress.

Before dealing with the alleged hereditary effects of partial vernalization, I must say a word about vernalization itself. Vernalization means the treatment of seeds of " winter " cereals—rye and wheat (i.e normally sown in autumn) so that they can be sown in spring, like normal " spring " strains, and produce a crop the same year. The method was discovered by a German called Gassner towards the end of the first World War[1]. Seeds are soaked by being put between moist filter-paper in Petri dishes, and then placed in a refrigerator for about three weeks, during which time they just begin their germination.

[1] Something similar was first described as long ago as 1854 in the U.S.A. (Sax. in [7] ; p. 143).

The resultant changes were studied by other research workers, notably by Gregory, of the Imperial College of Science at South Kensington. The incipient germination at low temperature alters the way the plant develops, notably in reducing the number of leaves that have to unfold before flowering can take place. Thus, in a winter strain of rye, untreated seeds sown in spring produce about 22 leaves, and by the time these are produced, the season is too advanced for the plant to produce a good " head." But vernalization treatment reduces the number to 12 and there is then time for the seeds to mature. Sowing the seeds in autumn, as is normally done, produces an effect similar to vernalization treatment : the young plant passes through a period of cold which reduces the number of leaves which precede flowering, so enabling the grain to be harvested the following summer.

Around 1930, Lysenko had the idea of turning these scientifically interesting results to practical account. He used a much reduced amount of water to soak the seeds (50 per cent. of the dry weight of seed to be treated), with the result that, although changes leading to a reduction in the number of leaves took place inside the seed, there was no visible germination. This meant that the treated seeds could be sown on a commerical scale, which is impossible with already germinated seeds.

This was one of the results for which Lysenko was honoured and promoted. Unfortunately, however, although the method worked nicely in the laboratory, it seems to have been a failure in practice. It is impossible to ensure that seeds treated *en masse* shall all get just the limited amount of soaking required; many remain dry and therefore unvernalized; many others become too wet, and germinate precociously. So the results were very uneven, and much seed was wasted; and the system now seems to have been abandoned as a practical method. We do not know whether it was ever used on a large scale: but Professor Ashby tells me that in 1945, when he was in the U.S.S.R. as Counsellor to the Australian Legation, a high official of the Comissariat of Agriculture told him that no vernalization was being practised on a commercial scale.

This surprised Ashby very much, since in the Sowing Decree, published in February of each year, it is always laid down that seed must be treated by Lysenko's " pre-treatment method." The mystery was solved when he got hold of a " Farmer's Leaflet," which explained how to carry out the method. The farmer is told to take a handful of grain from each of his sacks, put it on blotting paper, and count the proportion of seeds which germinate. In other words, the method is not pre-treatment at all—it is just an ordinary germination test.

It seems difficult to account for this use, or rather misuse, of the term *pre-treatment* except as an attempt by Lysenko to save face. It should be mentioned that there has never been any public statement as to the failure or abandonment of vernalization as a practical measure in the U.S.S.R. It should also be noted that, in spite of the fact that Lysenko's methods have been published and are well-known in 'capitalist' countries, agronomists there too have never been able to make a success of them in practice, although, as Dobzhansky writes, " not even Lysenko can accuse them of not wishing to increase their yields and their incomes."

In general, the practice outside the U.S.S.R. has been to adopt the methods of neo-Mendelism, namely the selective breeding of new stocks adapted to special climatic conditions, in preference to vernalization treatment (see Langdon-Davies, 1949, p. 92).

I now come to Lysenko's claim to have induced permanent hereditary changes by a modified vernalization treatment. Ordinary vernalization has never been found to have any hereditary effects, any more than any other ordinary treatment of seeds or growing plants. However, on the basis of his theoretical beliefs, Lysenko thought that it might be adapted to change the hereditary constitution of the strain. For some reason not apparent to western geneticists, he thought that a reduced time of treatment (about one instead of three weeks in the cold after soaking) would " shatter " the winter cereal's constitution so that it was then able to " assimilate " the changed conditions, and become converted in a few generations into a spring cereal which would go on behaving as a spring strain even without further treatment. This is his main claim to the production of a Lamarckian effect.

We must first recall that there is an enormous volume of negative evidence from the work of biologists in many countries, showing that, when proper scientific precautions are exercised, no evidence is obtained of any Lamarckian inheritance due to changed conditions, including special treatments.

Lysenko, unfortunately, did *not* exercise proper scientific precautions. As Waddington (1948–49) says, " the alleged hereditary changes are followed through too few generations, the genetical purity of the initial material is not adequately ensured, the possibility of selection is not always ruled out."

However, Waddington appears to me to have been over-cautious in this as well as in other judgments. I would say with assurance that selection was *never* ruled out, and that it must actually have been operative. Lysenko certainly has not taken the scientific precautions which in any western country would be regarded as elementary. In the first place he works with exceedingly impure strains. Ashby tells me that he has seen his experimental plots of cereals, and that they could only be described as " deplorable " : instead of attaining the strict uniformity which any careful experimenter can obtain, or even the reasonable uniformity which is necessary in order to draw firm conclusions, they were ragged, with a wide range of visible variation, and could obviously have been harbouring an equally high degree of invisible physiological variability.

With such a degree of inherent variability, it would be all too easy to breed only from those plants which behaved most closely like spring strains, and so to get the desired conversion—but by selection of already existent genetic differences instead of through the inheritance of the direct effect of the treatment. With highly impure (heterozygous) strains, the effect of selection might be rapidly cumulative, since new recombinations would be available over several generations.

No data are available as to the variability in behaviour of the strains when untreated—i.e. the number in the mixed stock which possessed ' spring ' tendencies anyway. Furthermore, Lysenko never seems to have employed adequate controls, or indeed in many cases any controls at all.

As Darlington (1947) pithily writes, " The evidence as a whole shows that Lysenko is making use of the three classical precautions needed for the ' success ' of experiments designed to prove the inheritance of environmental effects : namely, beginning with a mixed stock, omitting to use proper controls, and repudiating statistical tests."

Ashby has suggested to me a further interesting possibility—namely, that the seeds of the treated plants were automatically vernalized in the ear. We know that pre-germination changes can take place in seeds still in the plant ; and presumably the fruiting of the vernalized plants would take place later and therefore in lower temperatures than of unvernalized plants sown in autumn. If so, partial vernalization would continue to occur every year ; however, it would not be genetically determined, but would be due merely to similar conditions operating on each generation.

Such a simulation of the inheritance of acquired characters does actually take place in our own tendons. These are remarkable, in that their direction and their strength are always closely adapted to the strains to which they are subjected. However, there is no reason to suppose that this means that the size and direction of every tendon has been genetically predetermined. Paul Weiss showed that the cells of which tendons are composed, if grown in tissue-culture films subjected to a pattern of tensions, first orient themselves mainly along the directions of greatest tension, and then proceed to multiply more rapidly there than elsewhere. These are their only adaptive genetic properties. The details of size and direction of adult tendons are adaptive in effect, but result automatically from these two properties during the course of each individual's development ; neither natural selection nor Lamarckian inheritance is needed to explain them.

To sum up :—Vernalization itself is an established

fact. The scientific discovery underlying vernalization was made outside the U.S.S.R. Lysenko invented the actual method. But it does not appear to be of great practical importance. On the other hand, the hereditary conversion of winter into spring cereals through a few years' partial vernalization, as claimed by Lysenko, is *not* an established fact. Some of the results obtained are almost certainly due not to Lamarckian inheritance, but to the faulty methods and material used, which permitted selection to operate ; others may be due to developmental responses to the conditions in each generation. The onus is on Lysenko to repeat the experiments with proper precautions and taking account of these sources of error.

Lysenko also claims to be able to convert spring wheats into winter wheats (which are more frost-resistant) by sowing in autumn for two to four years, apparently without partial vernalization ([3] ; p. 40, p. 48). After pointing out that no examples are known of winter strains among hard wheats, he goes on to state that autumn planting for two to four years would convert a hard into a soft wheat, and apparently one of ' winter ' type. Let me quote his own words ([3] ; p. 48). " When experiments were started to convert hard wheat into winter wheat it was found that after two, three or four years of autumn planting (required to turn a spring into a winter crop) *durum* becomes *vulgare*, that is to say, one species becomes converted into another. *Durum* wheat with 28 chromosomes is converted into several varieties of soft 42 chromosome wheat, nor do we, in this case, find any transitional forms . . . the conversion of one species into another takes place by a leap."

Any competent biologist and any experienced

plant-breeder will be sceptical and indeed suspicious about this extraordinary claim to have achieved what one can only describe as mutational Lamarckism. Until the experiment is repeated with seed of known genetic purity and with rigorous precautions, a far simpler explanation is that the seed was of mixed type (or that some ' soft ' seeds were lying about in the soil) and the winter conditions killed off all but the winter-resisting types—a straightforward selectionist result.

I now come to Lysenko's claim that the hereditary constitution of two different varieties or species of plants can be somehow combined by grafting the two together. This alleged effect, which I have briefly mentioned in Chapter 1, he claims to be due to " vegetative hybridization " of the two " heredities," as opposed to the normal (sexual) hybridization obtained by cross-fertilization.

Ashby (1946) gives a description of Lysenko's methods and results, as seen by him personally in the glasshouses of the Institute of Genetics, while Crane (1949) who has done scientific research on grafting for many years at the famous John Innes Institution in London, may be referred to for a criticial analysis of the published results.

Tomatoes, and to a certain extent potatoes and other species of *Solanum*, have been used for the work. In one experiment, scions of a species with small fruits were grafted on to stocks of a variety of common tomato with large yellow fruits. In the next generation (F_1), seeds from the scions produced a few fruits almost as large as those of the stock. Seeds from these were sown, and produced a second (F_2) generation, with fruits as large as normal tomatoes. According to Lysenko, this means that the heredity of the tomato stock has "flowed into" the scion and changed its heredity.

It should be noted that only a few larger fruits were originally produced, which suggests that they were due to accidental cross-pollination from pure tomato stock (no precautions against this were taken). Further no seeds were sown from any but these larger fruits.

In a second experiment, both scion and stock were tomatoes. The scion had pinnate leaves and yellow fruits, the stock non-pinnate (potato-like) leaves and red fruits. Seeds were sown from the red fruits of the stock. Most of the plants were of the type of the stock, but "six had pinnate leaves, and some had yellow fruits" (we are not vouchsafed the information whether all or some of the plants with pinnate leaves also had yellow fruits, though this is obviously of some importance).

If the original stock had been heterozygous (hybrid) for the genes controlling leaf-shape and fruit-colour, we would, on elementary Mendelian theory, expect that some plants of the scion type might occur among the progeny. As no controls were raised, we cannot tell one way or the other ; but an interpretation on the basis of well-established principles is obviously the simpler, and we certainly cannot regard the experiment as proving anything new.

In another experiment, a yellow-fruited scion grafted on to a red-fruited stock is stated to have produced some plants with mottled red-and-yellow fruits and/or rose-coloured fruits. However, as Crane (1949) points out, the strain known as " Blood Orange " contains a gene which gives rise to fruits ranging from nearly yellow to nearly red, through all intermediate degrees of striping or mottling. And if the stock had been heterozygous for such a gene, the results would be accounted for on Mendelian lines. But as here again no controls were bred, and no precautions taken against cross-pollination, these experiments also prove nothing one way or the other.

However, when Ashby and I were in Moscow in 1945, we ascertained that the crucial grafting experiments of Avakyan and Yastreb, which though published in 1941, were then (and still are) the mainstay of Lysenko's evidence for vegetative hybridization, had been independently repeated in another laboratory in the U.S.S.R., with the same strain of tomatoes, but using adequate controls. In particular, numbers of plants of the strains used for stock and for scion were raised without grafting, and bred from. Ashby later investigated further, and found that the one positive result obtained was that the ungrafted controls produced just as many " new " forms as the grafted plants. In other words, the strains employed in Lysenko's Institute were genetically far from pure, " throwing " many variations without grafting ; and accordingly this genetic impurity, and not the grafting, would in fact account for many of the new forms which had turned up in Lysenko's experiments. He also ascertained that permission could not be obtained to publish the results, presumably because they threw doubt on Lysenko's conclusions.

A little later, Wilson and Witner (1946) repeated the same type of experiment with a number of combinations of tomato strains, all of which had been previously bred to a high degree of genetic purity. In this case, no results of the original grafting, either of stock or scion or vice versa, could be detected. There was thus no question of Lamarckian inheritance in later generations, as there was no initial effect to be inherited.

Other results claimed by Lysenko may be better

interpreted on the basis of established genetic principles than as establishing wholly new principles. We know, for instance, that in various plants, and especially in the Solanaceae, the group to which tomatoes and potatoes belong, so-called chimaeras are not uncommon. A chimaera is an organism in which tissue with one set of genetic properties exists side by side with tissues with different properties. Sometimes this condition results from grafting, the genetically different tissues of scion and stock becoming combined in shoots arising close to the actual place of the graft.[1] This was originally discovered by Winkler and by Baur in Germany, before the first world war, and analysed in detail later, e.g. by Jorgensen and Crane in England more than 20 years ago.

In other cases, as Asseyeva showed in the U.S.S.R. in the late '20's with potatoes, the genetic difference between the two types of tissue is caused by a somatic mutation—i.e. a mutation arising in a cell of the body. When this cell is part of a growing-point, it reproduces itself in its mutated condition and multiplies to form a whole tissue of the new type.

Sometimes the two kinds of tissue exist side by side in patches or stripes, sometimes one encloses the other, as a glove encloses a hand (periclinal chimaeras).

The reproductive cells of higher plants always arise from the layer of tissue below the outer layer or epidermis, so that curious results can be obtained in later generations, depending on whether one or more outer layers of a periclinal chimaera are genetically different from the rest.

[1] This is quite different from the effects claimed by Lysenko, which are stated to arise in organs remote from the place of the graft, and to involve actual fusion of " heredities " not merely juxtaposition of genetically different tissues.

These well-established facts, which depend on chromosomal (genic) differences in different tissues, may possibly account for some of the results found in Lysenko's Institute ; but, if we are to be sure, the grafting experiments must be repeated with the deliberate aim of checking this possibility.

In some cases not involving grafting, this interpretation certainly seems much more plausible than Lysenko's. For instance, Ashby (1946) saw work in progress on a variety of potato (" Zarnitsa "), whose tubers have a yellowish or yellowish-red skin or epidermis, and a white centre. Tubers were split longitudinally, and from one half all the ' eyes ' (buds) were cut out. When these ' eyeless ' halves were put in moist sand at a rather low temperature, they produced a few new (adventitious) buds. Such adventitious buds are entirely formed from tissues below the epidermis.

The unoperated and operated half-tubers were then planted. The ' eyes ' on the unoperated tubers produced plants with normal tubers (with coloured skins). But the adventitious buds on the operated tubers produced plants which had white-skinned as well as coloured tubers. The white tubers in their turn produce bigger plants, with many more tubers on them. Lysenko claims that the surgical treatment has "brought out a modified heredity."

Ashby noticed that the ' normal ' plants, from coloured tubers, had curled leaves with occasional yellow patches on them—common symptoms of certain virus diseases. He suggested to Lysenko that the original strain was really a periclinal chimaera, so that you would expect different genetic results from buds formed exclusively from the inner tissues. Further,

79

that it was infected by virus, but only in the outer layers : if so, Lysenko would have made a quite new discovery—that certain kinds of potatoes could be freed from virus disease by a surgical operation.

Lysenko replied, first that there was no such thing as a chimaera, and secondly that *virus* is a concept which is not accepted by Soviet biologists(!).

In another case, of a graft of tomato on to tobacco, Ashby suggested that the occasional abnormal fruits produced by the tomato might be due to the passage of the chemical substance nicotine through the conducting tissues from the tobacco plant to the tomato plant. This again would be very interesting, but would not be an ' alteration of heredity.'

It has also been suggested that some of Lysenko's results may be due to the passage of some self-reproducing substance between stock and scion. This may well be true. For instance, as Salaman and Le Pelley discovered in 1930, pieces of King Edward potatoes induce a virus disease in other strains. The simplest explanation of this is that some form of protein normally present (and not deleterious) in King Edwards is what Darlington (1948) calls a pro-virus—i.e. can multiply in alien tissues, causing harmful effects (Darlington, 1944). In other cases, as in grafts between bean species, a protein of the stock seems able to pass into the scion and establish itself there, not as a virus but as a beneficent plasmagene. However, even if some of Lysenko's results depend on a similar mechanism of protein molecules from one partner becoming self-reproducing units in the other, this would not have anything to do with the hybridization of two complete heredities by grafting, as he claims.

Finally, Crane (1949 *a*) draws attention to the fact

that in his own very extensive and painstaking work on grafting, carried out on a large range of plants and with full scientific precautions, no evidence of hereditary effects, let alone of vegetative hybridization, has ever been obtained.

There may be a few positive results of Lysenko's grafting work which are not due to faulty technique, to absence of scientific precautions, or to failure to understand the nature and behaviour of chimaeras or of viruses. But these will need confirmation by others, and above all analysis in the light of existing knowledge, not merely interpretation in terms of Michurin's and Lysenko's crude theories of hereditary constitutions being " shaken " by grafting and then " assimilating " each other or the influences of external conditions—theories which do not link up with the main body of biological science. In any case, Lysenko has provided no crucial evidence to prove that grafting can produce any fusion of the two " heredities " concerned, or can produce results incompatible with neo-Mendelian genetics.

I now come to the repudiation of the theory of probability and the rejection of the use of statistical methods.

Lysenko and his philosophic helper, Prezent, first attacked the whole notion of applying mathematics to biology in 1940 (Hudson & Richens, 1946, p. 17), and in the 1948 discussion he cited the employment of such techniques by the Mendelians as proof of their ideological heresy. When Ashby asked one of Lysenko's assistants for some statistical evidence in favour of the validity of the results he was claiming, the man replied that, since both Darwin's work and Michurin's work was convincing without statistics, why should any statistical evidence be required of Lysenko ? (Ashby, 1946).

At the outset, I must remind my readers that proper statistical methods are universally used by all western scientists wherever certain types of numerical results are demanded. There is no other way of checking whether your results are significant—whether they really prove anything or not. This holds for chemistry or physics as much as for biology. But in genetics, where often the only way of getting results is to count the numbers of different types resulting from an experiment, it is particularly indispensable. This makes it all the more curious that Lysenko will have nothing to do with such techniques. His attitude appears to be partly due to the fact that the theory of probability and the statistical precautions derived from it are concerned with the scientific analysis of " chance," and that Lysenko has not understood what chance means in this mathematical sense (see pp. 91-2 for further discussion of this point).

However, I feel that there must be other reasons, of an ideological nature. Otherwise the philosopher Prezent would not have joined Lysenko in the campaign, nor would the entire mathematical theory of probability, as also the indeterminacy principle in physics, have been subjected to attack from quite other quarters in the U.S.S.R. It may be that at the back of the minds of the political and ideological leaders of the U.S.S.R., there is a feeling that there is no place either for chance or for indeterminacy in Marxist ideology in general, or in particular, in science as conceived of by dialetical materialism—a feeling that there is no room for probability or accident in a system which claims certitude.

I do not know whether this is the right answer or not. To find out the basic reasons for the attack on probability theory would mean reading, digesting and analysing all that has been published in Russia on the subject, and that, though it would be well worth doing, I must leave to others. Meanwhile, I do know that Lysenko and his followers refuse to utilize the statistical methods derived from probability theory. In so doing they deprive themselves of an essential scientific tool, and make it impossible for scientists elsewhere to judge of the validity of the results which they claim. The failure to use appropriate statistical methods, whether it springs from ideological reasons or not, is definitely unscientific.

This brings me to point four—the repudiation of neo-Mendelism, first by Lysenko and now officially by the Communist Party of the U.S.S.R. This is what men of science from other countries will find it hardest to follow—or to swallow. I shall treat of this in a more general way in the next chapter ; but wish here to bring out some specific points concerning it which arose in the actual controversy. Throughout the discussion, Lysenko and his followers treat neo-Mendelism (or Morgano-Mendelism or whatever other title they apply to modern genetics) as a mere theory, in the sense of a hypothesis, not in the usual sense in which the term *theory* is used in science, of a set of conceptions tying together a vast body of experimental results and established laws; what is more, they treat it as a theory inspired primarily by philosophical and political principles hostile to Marxism and Communism, and not by the desire to find the simplest explanation of the facts of nature. It cannot be too strongly reiterated that neo-Mendelian genetics is not just a theory in either of these two restricted senses. Indeed, it can now rightly claim the title of genetics *tout court* as a branch of science in its own right (I may recall that what we now call simple bacteriology was for a time referred to as ' germ theory '). It consists, first, of a really portentous accumulation of facts, some of observation but the majority experimental ; then of the laws (such as those of segregation, independent assortment, linkage, etc.) which subsume many of the facts ; of the mathematical calculations (often later verified by experiment), which permit a quantitative understanding of the action of selection on Mendelian populations ; of the concepts and principles, such as those of material particulate inheritance (the theory of the gene), the principles of chromosome behaviour, and the principles of selection, which give the simplest general conceptual framework for interpreting the facts and laws ; and finally of the interpretations, some wholly successful, others more speculative but at least coherent, of the processes of species-formation and long-range evolutionary change, in terms of neo-Mendelism and selection.

I repeat that modern genetics, with its neo-Mendelian basis, is now an autonomous branch of science, covering much of the field of evolution as well as of individual inheritance. Thus in repudiating " Morgano-Mendelism," the Michurinites and the Communist Party of the U.S.S.R. have repudiated not a mere speculative hypothesis nor a theory motivated by other than scientific reasons, but a large body of tested scientific fact, and a number of well-validated scientific laws.

Sir Henry Dale (1949), in his letter of resignation from the U.S.S.R. Academy of Sciences, brings this point out admirably. " The whole great fabric of exact knowledge, still growing at the hands of those who have followed Mendel, Bateson and Morgan, is to be repudiated and denounced."

Further, he makes clear what are the real issues, by describing the action of the Academy as the "last attempt to suppress or to mutilate scientific truth in the interests of an extraneous creed," and by writing that "many of us . . . have been proud to think that there were no political frontiers or national varieties in a Science common to all the world, but this is now to be separated from 'Soviet Science' and repudiated as 'bourgeois' and 'capitalistic'."

Prof. H. J. Muller, probably the ablest and certainly the most all-round geneticist that the world has yet seen, has also resigned his corresponding membership.

The Academy, in its official replies, has descended to extraordinary depths for a scientific body. It calls both Dale and Muller "tools in the hand of reactionaries," and implies that they would have had to expect persecution in their respective countries if they had not resigned. It states that Sir Henry Dale has shown himself a partisan "of the theories which were in vogue in Hitlerite Germany, which served as pretext for so many sanguinary horrors, and are still defended by the upholders of slavery and racial discrimination such as the Americans, who wish to impose their hegemony on the world." It adds that all believers in progress will approve the measures taken "and to be taken" by the Academy "to destroy for ever the continuance of this criminal obscurantism."

This brings out the real issue—that the U.S.S.R. is judging scientific fact and theories, not on the basis of their verifiable truth or falsity, but in relation to a particular social or political philosophy; and that in order to discredit those parts of science which they consider inimical to that philosophy, even the highest scientific body does not hesitate to employ the most violent abuse.

Coming down to details, Hitler's appeal to Mendelism in support of his racial policy was scientifically quite unjustified ; for another, the fact of his having made such an appeal is entirely irrelevant to the truth or falsity of neo-Mendelian genetics as a branch of science ; and finally, most neo-Mendelians are anti-racist. Then it is untrue that " the Americans " believe in slavery. It is not the Americans as a whole, or the United States as a nation, but only various separate States of the Union that uphold anti-Negro discrimination. Further, the statement that the States ("the Americans") aim at world hegemony is really not very relevant (even if it were true) to Sir Henry's resignation.

Finally, the assertion that Sir Henry Dale's arguments " are not scientific in character, but are solely dictated by political motives and serve the anti-democratic and anti-Soviet campaign initiated in certain Western States " is an insult to common sense, as well as to Sir Henry personally and to the integrity of men of science in general [1].

[1] In the satirical Soviet magazine *Krokodil* (1949, No. 2, p. 16) there appears a cartoon. This shows an alchemist on one side with the legend " this is how alchemist-scientists used to try to obtain gold—without success." On the other side, is a " bourgeois-scientist," with a typewriter on the table, with a bottle of port beside it, a cigar in his mouth, and in his hand a cheque marked $10,000. The legend reads, " this is how contemporary bourgeois scientists (like Herman J. Muller and Henry Dale) obtained gold, with great success." Since there is, in his pocket, a document labelled "Against Michurin " and another on the table labelled "Against Lysenko," the implication is that Muller and Dale are hostile to Michurinism because they receive large sums of money for writing articles on the subject.

One misapprehension must be dealt with. Quite intelligent people often seem to think that, when a new theory wholly or partly replaces an old one, the whole fabric of the relevant branch of science has to be scrapped. That, of course, is quite incorrect. For example, the acceptance of relativity theory has not involved the jettisoning of classical Newtonian mechanics, but has in the great majority of cases only meant a slight correction, negligible for most purposes, in a number of its laws. The body of ascertained knowledge remains : it has merely to be rendered more exact and incorporated into a more extended whole. The same holds for neo-Mendelism : whatever new theories Lysenko or anyone else may contribute to genetics, the vast body of scientific fact comprised in neo-Mendelism remains as a contribution to our knowledge of the universe. (The difference between the two examples is that whereas Einstein has successfully introduced a radically new theory, or framework of ideas, to correlate the physical facts involved, there is at present no prospect of neo-Mendelian theory being overthrown by Lysenko's ideas—they are too vague to deserve the title of a framework—or, indeed, by any other general theory of genetics and evolution).

Here I suppose I should turn aside for a moment to consider the nature of scientific law, for that august body, the U.S.S.R. Academy of Sciences itself, has utilized the subject as a weapon against the neo-Mendelians. In its manifesto that I have already cited, it asserts that " *Weismannite-Morganist idealist teaching is pseudo-scientific because it* is founded on the notion of the divine origin of the world and *assumes eternal and unalterable scientific laws.*"

In the first place, even if both the statements were

true, the term *pseudo-scientific* would still be quite unjustified. Plenty of good scientific work has been done by believers in a divine creation and by believers in scientific laws as something eternally given and merely waiting to be discovered. But, of course, the assertion applies nominally only to neo-Mendelian "teaching," although, as has been earlier made clear, the term " teaching " in this controversy is unjustifiably extended to include the entire system involved—facts, laws, hypotheses and theories as well as underlying doctrine or philosophic tendency.

However, the statements simply are not true. I do not imagine that more than a handful of neo-Mendelian selectionists believe in the divine origin of the universe, and probably not one would believe in the divine origin of the world of living things as they exist to-day, whether through special creation or through a supernatural control of the process of evolution. This I know to be true of Morgan and Muller ; and if I may take this occasion of affirming my own position, I have always believed (on the principle of William of Occam's razor) in the natural origin of living from non-living matter on this planet, and I consistently maintained, even through the sceptical period that ended around 1930, the view that Lamarckism was untrue, but that the evolution of life can be explained in terms of mutation and natural selection ; and I am philosophically a non-theist. In any event, how can a belief in God or in creation affect the truth or falsity of scientific laws ?

We now come to the second statement. I am extremely puzzled to imagine what possible authority or evidence the Academy has for its assertion that neo-Mendelism (" Weismannite-Morganist tendency ") assumes eternal and unalterable scientific laws. Just after I had taken my university degree, I used to go down occasionally to the John Innes Horticultural Institution to help Bateson count peas from his genetic experiments, and I can vouch for the fact that his and Punnett's formulation of the laws of coupling and repulsion, as they used then to be called, was not based on any metaphysical concept of scientific law. For them, as for myself or any other neo-Mendelian I can think of, the formulation of a law is an attempt to translate into general, and if possible simple and also quantitative terms, any regularities which they may discover in the phenomena they are investigating. Once a law is formulated, its validity (or otherwise) can be tested against new phenomena and its accuracy improved, or its short-comings or its fallacy exposed. There is nothing external or unalterable about it. It is a short-hand way of stating that, in certain circumstances, certain results have been observed in the past, and can be expected in the future. Mendel's second law, the laws of independent assortment, for example, subsumes the following facts: when a cross occurs between animals or plants showing normal sexual reproduction and exhibiting normal chromosomal behaviour at meiosis, then, for characters dependent on genes not lodged in the same chromosome and not linked with the main gene or genes for sex-determination, we can in the F_2 generation expect a quantitative distribution approximating to that to be calculated on the assumption that the separation of any one chromosome-pair at meiosis has no effect on that of any other. But alter the circumstances, and the law will alter. If the characters affect viability, the proportions in F_2 will change from expectation ; if two or more of the genes are in the same chromosome, they will not assort independently ; if the meiotic process be upset, whether by tetraploidy, by directive non-random segregation of chromosomes, etc., the law will not hold. And, of course, the law could not have existed before sexually reproducing organisms with differentiated chromosomes had been evolved. Nor, in the view of most men of science, did it (as opposed to the phenomena which it subsumes) exist before it was actually formulated by the early Mendelians.

This brings me to another point concerning scientific laws. As work on a subject is pursued, the laws concerning it tend to appear less and less important, but become merged into a larger construction, a broad theory, or a vast system of phenomena all interrelated on the basis of certain simple and fundamental facts and conceptions. Thus what neo-Mendelians are concerned about is not whether the laws of segregation or of independent assortment are eternal or unalterable, but whether or not their labours have produced a large and important body of new truth. In this, large bodies of phenomena are elucidated on the basis of the following elementary facts : (a) the existence of discrete material units of heredity lodged in a definite order in the chromosomes ; (b) the constancy (complete self-reproduction) of these units save for occasional mutations (incomplete self-reproduction) ; (c) the differential viability and differential reproduction of organisms containing different contributions of these units. The great majority of the multifarious phenomena of heredity and evolution are now seen as consequential extensions, in various circumstances, of these few basic factual principles.

Curiously enough, Babajanyan takes a quite different view. (It does not seem to matter to the Michurinites whether their statements are mutually contradictory). He says ([3]; p. 163) "The very foundation of Mendelism-Morganism is the principle that biological laws are unknowable "—a somewhat curious assertion about the science which has for the first time succeeded in establishing quantitative laws for the phenomena of heredity.

The insistence that neo-Mendelism is wedded to the idea of eternal and unalterable laws is all the more strange, since one of Lysenko's main arguments against it (1948) is that its " so-called laws . . . are *based entirely on chance* [italics his], mutation, the separation of the *so-called paternal and maternal chromosomes* [italics mine] at meiosis, fertilization [and, he might have added, under natural selection] being all matters of chance. Thus *living nature appears to the Morganists as a medley of fortuitous isolated phenomena without any necessary connection and subject to no laws*. Chance reigns supreme . . . Unable to reveal the laws of living nature, the Morganists have to resort to the theory of probabilities, and since they fail to grasp the concrete content of biological processes, they reduce biological science to mere statistics . . . With such a science it is impossible to plan to work towards a definite goal. Physics and chemistry have been rid of fortuities. That is why they have become exact sciences. *By ridding our science of Mendelism-Morganism we will expel fortuities from biological science*. We must firmly remember that *science is the enemy of chance* " [italics his].

Apart from the fact that the accusation of failing to grasp the concrete content of the subject seems singularly inapplicable to the latest discoveries of cytogenetics as regards the actual chemistry of the hereditary material, utterances like these reveal an extraordinary scientific illiteracy. Every elementary student is aware that the exactitude of many of the laws of physics and chemistry (such as the gas laws) depends on the fact that they are statistical laws—in other words, ' matters of chance.' When the physicists are no longer dealing with statistical laws, but are confronted with individual phenomena, regularity ceases, and chance (but now in the sense of individual accident) begins to reign. Lysenko is, of course, using the word *chance* in different senses and applying it to different scales of phenomena. (see also p. 82)

To return for a moment to the subject of ' eternal laws,' it is possible that the Academy was not referring to what are usually called the laws of Mendelism, but to some supposed law of the non-inheritance of acquired characters. If so, this is again incorrect. In the first place, no such law has been formulated. Some neo-Darwinians have pointed out the logical impossibility of the inheritance of acquired characters in the commonly accepted sense of the word (modifications of the individual due solely to changed environment or to changed habits), and R. A. Fisher has mathematically demonstrated the impossibility of such inheritance, even if it did occur, accounting for the observed facts of evolution. But, more important, no neo-Mendelian of whom I am aware denies the possibility that the hereditary constitution might, in exceptional cases, be *directively* altered by agencies external to it—that is, not merely altered in a way unrelated to the agent as by all known mutagens, but altered relatedly, or even in some cases adaptively. One of the speakers in the debate expressed great surprise that a leading Morganist had gone so far against the principles ascribed to him by the Michurinites as to discuss the possibility of inducing related hereditary changes by means of antigens, as claimed by Guyer and Smith. I well remember the incident, since Carr-Saunders and I spent a great deal of time in repeating the work—unfortunately with entirely negative results. But no one believed in the existence of any eternal law which would prevent its being true.

As regards the fifth point—the taking over as evidence for Michurinite theory of practical results which are better explicable in Mendelian terms—I may cite the successful results quoted by various speakers (Lysenko himself, Yakushkin, Feiginson, Lukyanenko, Petrov, Krylov, etc.) as accruing in crop-plants from intervarietal hybridization followed by selection. This is always quoted against the neo-Mendelians as a Michurinite method. The fact is, of course, that in using this method (which in certain cases gives excellent results) the Michurinites are, without knowing it, simple utilizing the basic Mendelian principles of segregation and recombination, followed by the principles of Darwinian selection, but undiluted by any trace of Lamarckism[1].

(Luther Burbank, also a declared opponent of Mendelism, scored his successes by a very similar utilization of Mendelian phenomena).

A similar comment may be made on the results

[1] The wide crosses carried out by Michurin himself were made for the most part with fruit-trees. In these, owing to differences in chromosome-number and to the existence of self-sterility and incompatibility mechanisms, the hybrid is very rarely fertile. This does not prevent Lysenkoites from claiming that the same mysterious ' qrinciple ' operates both in these and in fully fertile crosses. " Bourgeois geneticists," of course, often apply neo-Mendelian principles consciously. A good example is the building up of a much improved strain of tobacco, *Roundtip*, by East and Jones through selection following a cross between two other varieties (see A. H. Shull, *Heredity*, p. 233).

proclaimed by various speakers (for example, Yudin, Greben, Minkevich, Shaumyan, Chekmenev, Feiginson, Ushakova, etc.). In general, they claim their results as a proof of Michurinism, or of the efficacy of Lysenko's methods of selection[1]. However, so far as I can understand from the summaries of their remarks, the results were achieved by straightforward selection, such as might be practised by any neo-Darwinian breeder. It is true that their successes are often contrasted with the ' failures ' of the Russian Morgano-Mendelians ; but these, in so far as truly failures, are presumably due to the latter having attempted to apply their principles in a faulty way. Especially in the early stages of modern genetics, the complexity of practical problems was not always grasped, nor the need for selection in relation to a particular environment. The great majority of neo-Mendelians to-day would agree with Lysenko's own formulation of the matter. He writes (1948) : " Our science and practice of animal breeding . . . must be guided by the principle *to select and improve breeds in accordance with the conditions of feeding, maintenance and climate* " [italics his]. This, by itself, is impeccable from the neo-Mendelian and neo-Darwinian stand-point, although his further condition, that one must " create conditions of feeding and maintenance most suitable to the given breeds," which in practice seems to mean merely providing a rich nutrition, is dictated by his Lamarckian beliefs, and could have no selective effect in the genetic sense.

Some other scientific aspects of the discussion may be briefly mentioned—the coining of the term *autogenesis*, unknown or at least unused, so far as I am aware,

[1] Mr. Richens tells me that the Russian word *seleksija* means breeding in general. It is impossible to judge from the reports whether speakers were not sometimes using " selection " in this sense.

in the West, to denote what Lysenko believes to be the belief of his opponents as to the determination of development and evolution entirely by intrinsic factors. Thus Perov ([3]; p. 141) says that " the reactionary school, the formalist Morganist geneticists, advanced the idea of the autogenetic factor in evolution. It is claimed that the factor is the form of some principle which conditions the entire process of development of the living organism independently of its environment, and even of the soma of the organism itself." The last clause is entirely unintelligible to me, since the soma is that which undergoes the process of development. And as for Perov's assertion that the neo-Mendelians believe that development is independent of environment, he has either never taken the trouble to look at any textbook of genetics, or else is being guilty of deliberate misrepresentation. In respect of evolution, almost all neo-Darwinians believe firmly in the guiding activity of the environment, mediated through natural selection, so that the " creative " aspect of evolution in producing novelty is due not only to the new bricks of the building provided by the " autogenetic " process of mutation, but also to the directives furnished by the inorganic and biological environment to the moulding force of selection.

In general, the controversial methods of Lysenko and his followers are unfair or unscientific, in that their attacks are almost always directed against the youthful and sometimes crude neo-Mendelism of 20 to 40 years ago, when it was groping towards new facts and more comprehensive formulations, and that they have either deliberately neglected its remarkable modern developments, or have not taken the trouble to understand them (see Stern, 1949).

The rejection of the concept of pure lines, in spite of its experimental verification and theoretical validation, may be due merely to wish-fulfilment, or more probably to the fact that what the Lysenkoites have called pure lines in the U.S.S.R. are not really such at all, and therefore *are* capable of modification through selection ; but it can certainly not be justified as a scientific procedure. Nor can the condemnation of inbreeding as a practical method be justified. It is even more difficult to suggest a motive for this, especially as it has been applied so very successfully in the United States to maize, and is now beginning to be applied (for example, by Henry Wallace) to fowls. Yet Serebrovsky is critized by Perov for advocating inbreeding in poultry; and Feiginson, the Scientific Director of the Mordovian Plant-Breeding Station, incorrectly stated that the above-mentioned work on maize had nothing to do with Mendelian theory. He said, " All that the Morganists proposed was certain intricate technical methods of obtaining such maize seeds (preliminary self-pollination and selection of self-pollinated strains), which were very difficult to apply on a mass scale. This, obviously, suits the interests of capitalist seed firms, since in capitalist countries the methods proposed by the Morganists are beyond the capacity of the ordinary farmer."

The methods may be beyond the capacity of the ordinary farmer, but, as mentioned elsewhere (p. 127) it is very much in the interests of the ordinary farmer and of the community as a whole that they should be adopted by the organizations, such as plant-breeding stations, which should be competent to do so.

As an example of peculiar scientific reasoning, I should like to quote from the interview given by

Lysenko in 1947 on intra-specific competition (reprinted in [2] ; p. 157). For one thing, he contradicts himself. At one place he says that there is no struggle (competition) between organisms with dissimilar needs, e.g. between carnivores and herbivores ; but on the next page he cites, as an example of intra-specific struggle or competition between species, the fact that wolves eat hares.

But his main point is that there is no such thing as *intra*-specific *struggle*, i.e. competition, between individuals or types belonging to the same species. Considering that this is the only basis on which selection could operate in nature, this is, to say the least of it, surprising. But perhaps Lysenko has never throught the matter out to the extent of realizing that the intra-specific struggle for existence is a somewhat metaphorical phrase, denoting the differential survival of different types which happen to exist within the species. Furthermore, he is apparently unaware of the various examples of intra-specific competition which have been experimentally demonstrated (see Huxley, 1942, pp. 95, 468, etc.). One of the simplest cases is provided by the adaptation of bacteria to new conditions, which is now known to be due in some cases to the differential survival of a mutant type in competition with the unmutated standard type. [1]

But the high point of his argument deserves citing verbatim (my translation from the French). " How are we to explain the importance assigned by bourgeois biology to the " theory " of intra-specific competition ?

[1] It should be mentioned that the recent work of Hinshelwood seems to establish that in other cases, the entire population " mutates " adaptively. Such a result is possible in the simplest organisms, but apparently not in those in which chromosomes have been differentiated as " organs of heredity."

The reason is that it has to justify the fact that, in capitalist societies, the majority of the population lives a wretched existence, especially during periods of over-production." Comment on this fantastic and un-supported assertion is superfluous.

It is on a par with the statement of Glushchenko in *Pravda* on April 5, 1948 (summarized in the *New York Herald Tribune* of April 6) that American geneticists have developed theories of over-population to justify American imperialist expansion. " The servility of the American Morganists and Weismannists to American imperialism is especially clear in the problem of so-called over-population. American monopolists have to justify before the masses their aspirations for world domination. That is why their Morganist-Weismann-ist hirelings resurrect the reactionary ideas of Malthus and raise a hullabaloo about *the over-population that they themselves have invented*." And Glushchenko claims to be a man of science ! He might be asked to investigate the demographic situation in countries such as Haiti, Italy, Tunisia, or Egypt before making such ludicrous assertions.

I would also like to cite a statement which I find scientifically and, indeed in every respect, incom-prehensible. Yudin is summarized ([1] ; p. 654) as saying that ' the principle of vegetative hybridization is important in animal husbandry ' [1].

[1] I can now quote his verbatim remarks ([3] ; p. 412). He says that the arguments advanced by Zavadovsky " to prove that it is impossible to apply the principle of vegetative hybridization to animal breeding are to my mind groundless and were prompted by his narrow con-ception of the problem. *Vegetative hybridization must not be reduced to the mere grafting of tissues*. A broader view of vegetative hybridization must be taken. *Properly speaking*, it is the influence of the Soma upon future generations." So you can have " vegetative hybridization " without hybridization ! This is only one among many examples of looseness of thought and misuse of scientific terms which enables the Michurinites to fit almost anything into their ' doctrine.'

But I must now pass to Lysenko himself, for his personal role has been of unusual importance. I will not attempt to deal with the details of his theory of heredity and evolution, as that has been discussed elsewhere (for example, by Hudson and Richens, 1946 ; Ashby, 1947 ; Darlington, 1947). The fact is relevant, however, that it is an essentially naive and *simpliste* theory, based on analogy rather than on induction. In his own words (1948) : " *heredity is the effect of the concentration of the action of external conditions assimilated by the organism in a series of preceding generations* " [italics his]. Heredity is " inherent in any particle of the living body." Yet (though in general he denies any special genetic role whatever to the chromosomes) in one place he admits that heredity is " transmitted through the chromosomes in the sexual process," without seeing that, the chromosomes being what they are, namely the vehicles of a row of spatially or chemically differentiated unit-sectors or genes, this admission has as its direct consequence the various laws of neo-Mendelian genetics. He speaks contemptuously of Mendel's laws as " the pea laws," and in the 1939 discussion on genetics referred to the 3 : 1 ratio as " the work of a devil." However, though he must accept the evidence of his senses through the microscope as to the existence of chromosomes, he refuses to admit genes. He himself simply ignores them ; but his philosophical helper, Prezent, as noted elsewhere (p. 51), categorically denies the reality of their existence.

It should be noted that this admission of the existence of chromosomes is the only common element between Lysenko and the neo-Mendelians. Otherwise he prefers to throw everything overboard and start again from scratch —assuredly not a very advanced scientific procedure.

99

I said that it is relevant that this theory is naive in type, for Lysenko would be the first to repudiate any claim to be an intellectual. He is a peasant, with a passion for practical results in his work. He is also an ambitious' man. He has not had any advanced scientific education, but has come to science from practical agriculture. He is politically a zealous communist, and also a powerful one, having been for a period a Vice-President of the Supreme Soviet. A Russian scientist described him to me as the Rasputin of Russian biology ; but after listening to him and talking with him, I am sure that this is wrong : Savonarola would fit better, though by no means perfectly. He is, I am sure, sincere ; but he is certainly fanatical and I should imagine ruthless.

Since writing the above, I came across the following description of Lysenko given by Ashby (1947, p. 116) on the basis of considerably more experience. "And what of Lysenko the man ? Can we, Russian fashion, analyse his motives as he so often analyses those of his opponents ? He is not a charlatan. He is not a showman. He is not personally ambitious. He is extremely nervous and conveys the impression of being unhappy, unsure of himself, shy, and forced into the role of leader by a fire within him. He believes passionately in his own theories, and he is not convinced by cold reasoning. He describes his own writing as always impartial, although passionate, and the writing of his opponents as ' passionless, cold-blooded and measured, yet extremely partial.' He identifies his work with the welfare of Soviet agriculture, so that any attack on him he interprets as an attack on the Soviet state. He is fired by his mission to scourge bourgeois genetics out of Russia, because he really believes it is harmful. He was aptly described to me by one who knew him well as ' like Savonarola.' The ' new genetics ' is an interesting example of the grave danger of departing from the familiar methodology of science, and approaching natural phenomena with the mind already made up. Just as Krenke's work [on plant development] is a legitimate and profitable use of dialectics in science, so Lysenko's work is an exploitation of dialectics in science for political ends. The ends may be justified ; Lysenko may be doing a great job for Russia. But the bulk of his opinions on genetics may be dismissed as the products of a medieval mind using what is almost a medieval technique."

I would like to put on record one incident which I personally witnessed. During the Academy celebrations in 1945, I had asked to see Lysenko and his results, but had been told that he was too busy. However, after repeated requests, it was suddenly announced that he would lecture next day, and I went to listen, accompanied by Prof. Ashby, and by an excellent interpreter who was also a biologist. Her running translation was at one moment drowned by a burst of laughter from the large and distinguished audience. On my asking her afterwards what had provoked this, it appeared that Lysenko was discussing Mendelian dominance and segregation, which his opponents sometimes brought up against him. Dominance, he said, was easy to explain on his own theories; it was the "assimilation " (or perhaps " digestion "—I forget which) of one heredity by a second, after a cross. But segregation (of recessive characters in F_2) ? That also was easy. " We know in our own persons," he said, " that assimilation (or digestion) is not always complete. When that is so, what happens ? We belch. *Segrega-*

tion is Nature's belching ; unassimilated hereditary material is belched out " (presumably in a 1 : 3 ratio !). I cite this remark as further evidence of the fact that, scientifically, Lysenko can only be described as illiterate. I use the word as meaning that it is impossible to discuss matters with him on a scientific basis, as appeared in Ashby's and my subsequent conversations with him, and is evident throughout his remarks at the session. Sometimes he appears ignorant of the scientific facts and principles involved, sometimes he misunderstands them, sometimes he distorts them, sometimes he counters them with bare assertions of his own beliefs.

Immediately after the lecture, on which he took notes, Ashby made a careful summary of it, a copy of which I possess. The following brief extracts are further illustrations of the naive and unscientific (or perhaps I had better say pre-scientific) nature of Lysenko's reasoning : " Different organisms demand different food, and that is evidence of their different heredity." " There is no organ of heredity : there is no hereditary matter separate from the soma. There are organs of reproduction but no organs of heredity." " Since the molecules [of the organism] are built from its food, therefore by regulating metabolism we can regulate heredity. There cannot be such a miracle as a change in the body of an organism without there being a consequent change in its heredity." " We do not believe what the [Mendelian] geneticists claim—that phenotypes can differ but their offspring remain the same." " Why do some workers fail to obtain these results [those claimed by Lysenko] with vegetative hybrids ? It is simply because they do not *want* to . . . if you concentrate on getting certain results, you will obtain them."

I am glad to be confirmed, in my opinion of Lysenko, by Dr. Harland, one of the world's most eminent men in the fields both of pure and applied genetics, who in a letter to *Discovery* (1949) writes as follows : " In 1933 . . . I saw Lysenko in Odessa, catechized him for several hours and inspected his practical work. It was quite clear that Lysenko was blazingly ignorant of the elementary principles of both plant physiology and genetics. . . You simply couldn't talk to Lysenko—it was like discussing the differential calculus with a man who did not know his 12-times table. When I say that some of his assistants were using plant pots without drainage holes, you amateur gardening readers will understand.

"After much persuasion Lysenko gave me a formula for vernalizing cotton seed. After giving the method a full trial, we found that it just didn't work . . . " (As already mentioned, Ashby in 1945 ascertained that vernalization of cereals was not being employed practically, apparently because Lysenko's method, though satisfactory in laboratory conditions, could not be satisfactorily adapted to large-scale practice).

I will conclude with one further example of Lysenko's scientific illiteracy—by which I mean his inability or refusal to grasp what his opponents are talking about, or to understand the significance of scientific facts— concerning the use of colchicine in genetics. Colchicine is a chemical substance by means of which plants can be made to double their chromosome-number. This induced polyploidy itself brings about changes in the characters of the strain, some of which may be valuable. But perhaps its chief use is in rendering possible fertile crosses between varieties or species with different chromosome-numbers. Thus, while a cross between forms with 2n and 4n chromosomes respectively would be sterile, if the 2n form has its chromosome-number doubled, the cross will be between two forms with the same chromosome-number, and will be fertile. The new genetic combinations thus made possible are sometimes of considerable practical value.

The effect of colchicine appears to be due to the slowing down or immobilizing of certain processes of cell-division, and has no detectable ill effects either at the time or afterwards. However, this is how Lysenko refers to the method (Biol. Rasvitia Rasten's 1940, p. 287). " By treating plants with a very powerful poison, colchicine, and other torturing applications they [the neo-Mendelians] mutilate plants." He also added that colchicine treatment was of no practical value. He appears not to have changed his views since 1940.

The use of words like *torturing*, *mutilation*, and *maiming*, though doubtless useful as a means of arousing prejudice, is scientifically irrelevant, and entirely misleading as applied to a treatment which in no way prevents the plant from exercising any of its normal functions.

As recorded by Harland in his broadcast on the genetics controversy (summarized by Langdon-Davies, 1949, p. 87) Vavilov himself acted as interpreter between him and Lysenko. After the unsatisfactory discussion which I have just cited, Vavilov said to Harland, smiling, " Lysenko is an angry species ; all progress in the world has been made by angry men, so let him go on working . . . He does no harm and may some day do good."

Alas, Vavilov was too tolerant. Lysenko has done a great deal of harm, to Vavilov himself as well as to genetical science.

My interpretation of Lysenko's role in the matter is as follows. He genuinely believes that he has obtained the inheritance of acquired characters by certain special treatments, and that he has been successful in effecting vegetative hybridization by means of grafting. Neither of these results would be possible on the basis of neo-Mendelian fact and theory in their present form. On the other hand, as already pointed out, the results might have been obtained owing to the non-observance of certain procedural precautions in the crucial experiments.

Lysenko, in my opinion, has not understood the solidity of neo-Mendelism as a system or a branch of science, how massive and yet how complex it is, how well-grounded in fact and how well-checked by mathematical deduction. He has only seen that its proponents are hindering his work, in which he genuinely believes. Sooner than have his experiments repeated with new and adequate precautions, sooner than take the trouble to try to reconcile the two ' opposites ' involved ; above all, sooner than admit that he may have been mistaken, and that living nature is not so easily taken by storm, he had made up his mind to treat neo-Mendelism as the enemy, and to root it out from the U.S.S.R., so as to leave the field free for his own ideas.

On the other hand, however energetic and however powerful Lysenko may be, he could not have accomplished this feat without political backing. But this leads us away from science and into political and ideological fields ; and to discuss these aspects of the controversy requires a separate chapter.

CHAPTER 4

GENETICS AS A SCIENCE

In this chapter I shall endeavour to give some account of the development of genetics to show what is meant by calling it a science. It is not " just a theory " or a set of untested hypotheses or points of view, but an organized body of scientific knowledge—in other words, a science in its own right. And since most of modern genetics is neo-Mendelian, a good deal of the discussion will deal with neo-Mendelism.

Neo-Mendelism consists in the first place of a quite enormous body of factual data ; in the second place of a number of laws which subsume those data in a convenient way ; in the third place of a body of what I may call mathematical data, derived from the application of mathematical reasoning to the facts and laws ; and finally of a general theory, or overall framework of concepts, which gives the simplest general explanation of all the observed facts and separate laws.

The factual data consist primarily of the results of thousands, or more probably tens of thousands, of experiments, recorded in scientific journals all over the world during the past fifty years ; secondly of innumerable facts of observation in the fields of systematics, palaeontology, and comparative anatomy, which can be regarded as the results of Nature's experiments in genetics over many generations—in other words, of evolution ; and thirdly of facts of observation and analysis concerning the structure, behaviour, and chemical nature of the chromosomes and genes—in other words of the physical basis of inheritance.

Every year, many of these experiments are repeated and many of the facts of observation checked, by hundreds or more probably thousands of students, during the practical laboratory work which forms part of the courses in biology in all modern universities.

Mendel's original experiment with peas provided a number of factual data—for instance, that when he crossed yellow and green-seeded peas, all the F_1 (first generation hybrid) had yellow seeds, but the F_2 (second generation) showed yellows and greens in a ratio approximating to $3 : 1$. A number of workers later repeated the same experiment, and obtained the same result.

Numerous other contrasting characters were later tested in an immense variety of animals and plants, and in many of these the same general phenomenon was observed, of uniformity in the first generation, followed by a three-to-one ratio in the second inbred generation.

All these facts are subsumed in what is generally called Mendel's First Law, the Law of Segregation. This means, that, whatever factors in the hereditary constitution are responsible for the appearance of characters that behave in this way, they must persist from generation to generation without contaminating or diluting each other, and must segregate, or separate from each other, when the time comes for forming the sexual cells or *gametes*.

In symbolic form, if Y is the factor for yellow seeds and y that for green, then the F_1 from YY and yy plants will all be Yy (and will appear yellow, since Y is what is called *dominant*, and masks the effects of the less potent, or *recessive y*). Its gametes will be *either*

pure Y or pure y ; each kind will have an equal chance
of fertilizing or being fertilized ; and so the F_2 will be
made up of four types, in theoretically equal numbers—
YY, Yy, yY, and yy. The first ·three will all *appear*
yellow, though two of them will be carrying the recessive factor for green, but the fourth will have green
seeds (and will breed true if selfed). A 3 : 1 ratio is thus
to be expected in F_2.

Seven other geneticists have repeated the same
experiment with yellow and green peas. The totals
found in all the experiments, including Mendel's, were
as follows :—Total seeds counted in F_2, 205,147 :
yellows, 153,902, greens, 51,245. Ratio of. yellows
to greens, 3.003 to 1. In other words, the observed
ratio differs from that expected on theoretical grounds
by only 1/10th of 1 per cent.—a remarkable concordance.

This law can be checked in various ways, of which I
will only mention one. If a hybrid F_1 is backcrossed
to the pure recessive parent, then the law of segregation
should give a 1 : 1 ratio. In our example, parents of
constitution Yy and yy should produce gametes Yy
and yy respectively ; and chance unions between these
should give 50 per cent. Yy and 50 per cent. yy, or a
1 : 1 ratio of yellow to green. The results conform to
the theoretical expectation.

Another set of experiments established the fact that
wholly new combinations of characters could be produced in the second or later generations from a cross
involving two or more separately segregating characters.
To use Mendel's data once more, from a cross between
yellow-seeded dwarf peas and green-seeded tall peas,
the new combinations *yellow tall* and *green dwarf* could
be extracted, and could be extracted as pure-breeding

lines. All the thousands of facts of this sort are subsumed in Mendel's Second Law, the Law of Independent Assortment, which implies that the various factor-units concerned segregate independently of each other.

In other cases, the assortment is not at random, and characters that go into a cross together come out together more frequently than they ought to if their segregation were independent ; the factors involved are said to be *linked*. If I may take a personal example, the 1,293 specimens of a little brackish-water shrimp, *Gammarus chevreuxi*, which I bred and counted in 1921 at Oxford, showed that the factor concerned with the presence or absence of any colour in the eye, and that determining whether the colour, if present, shall be black or red, tended to stick together thus in later generations after crossing. All such facts are subsumed under the various laws of linkage.

These various laws had been well established for a wide range of animal and plant species in the first 10 or 12 years after the rediscovery of Mendel's results in 1900. Meanwhile several biologists had drawn attention to the fact that they might all be explained as the result of the observed manœuvres of the microscopic bodies termed *chromosomes* (so-called because of the lucky fact that they take up various stains very readily after suitable treatment, and are therefore readily visible through the microscope).

Chromosomes were first properly investigated in the 1880's. Before 1890 the basic facts concerning their behaviour in cell-fusion and in sexual reproduction had been established, and by 1900 they had been demonstrated in the nuclei of the cells of all higher animals and plants examined for them.

Each species was found to have a constant number of chromosones, normally in pairs. Thus the number of chromosome-pairs in man is 24 ; in the famous fruit-fly, *Drosophila melanogaster*, of which many millions have now been bred and counted in genetical experiments, it is 4 ; and 7 in the garden pea used by Mendel.

We may conveniently compare the chromosomes to playing cards. Then, in all higher organisms, the fertilized egg and all the cells of the individual to which it gives rise, typically have two packs or complete sets of chromosomes in their nuclei. But before the gametes are formed, a complicated process of pairing and separation takes place, so that each gamete has only one pack of chromosomes, but a complete pack containing one of every kind. This process is called *meiosis*, meaning reduction (to half the number of chromosomes). And of course fertilization brings two packs together, one from the egg and the other from the sperm, and restores the double number once more.

It was soon realized that Mendel's two laws would be realized if the factors of heredity (or *genes*, as they were later conveniently called) were lodged in the chromosomes, and if each kind of gene could exist in a number of slightly different forms, or *allels*. The first law applies to one pair of genes (to be quite precise, to the pair of allels of one kind of gene) in one kind of chromosome, the second law to two or more pairs of genes lodged in different kinds of chromosomes.

Morgan and his school then suggested that if the genes were strung out in a single row within the chromosomes, the laws of linkage should apply to two or more pairs of genes which were lodged in one and the same kind of chromosome. And more detailed observation of the behaviour of chromosomes later showed that at meiosis the members of each chromosome pair twine round each other and exchange segments of their length, in precisely the way which would account for the numerical facts of linkage[1].

As a result, the chromosome theory of heredity was born, combining the facts drawn from breeding experiments with those derived from microscopic observation. It became possible to construct " chromosome maps " giving the relative positions of the genes (factors) within the chromosomes. This was done by taking the closeness of linkage between different kinds of genes as some measure of the physical distance between them along the chromosome's length.

The chromosome theory, like any scientific theory, has predictive functions : if it is true, then certain results should follow. These predictions can be tested. When fulfilled, they provide further confirmation for the general framework of concepts which we call the theory : when they are not fulfilled exactly, the theory has to be amplified or slightly modified. Of course, if results are obtained which are incompatible with the theory, the theory has to be scrapped and a new one substituted (as Newtonian mechanics has been replaced by relativity theory). But so far nothing of the kind has happened with the chromosome theory ; on the contrary, it is now buttressed with so many new supporting and confirmatory facts that it would appear impregnable.

I have already mentioned how its prediction that a cross involving two allels of the same kind of gene

---

[1] Actually, the chromosomes have divided longitudinally before pairing, so that there are four members of each kind of chromosome involved in the exchange process. For the details of the process, I must refer my reader to the text-books, as they are too complex to set forth here.

would give F_2 segregation in a 3 : 1 ratio, has been confirmed. As further examples of its predictive value, I may give the following : There are, in man as well as in many animals and a few plants, a number of so-called sex-linked characters, of which the most celebrated example is human hæmophilia (though certain kinds of human colour-blindness are more common), which appear only or normally in one sex, but are transmitted to the next generation only by the other : hence the exclusively male hæmophilics or " bleeders " in various royal families of Europe. On the chromosome theory one can prophesy just how such characters ought to be handed down the generations. One can also prophesy that if two or more characters show linkage with sex, they will show linkage with each other. And these predictions are verified by experience and experiment.

Again, on the chromosome theory, the 3 : 1 ratio of Mendel's first law is due to the behaviour and manœuvres of the single pair of chromosomes normally involved. Accordingly if one were dealing with four members of one kind of chromosome instead of two, the ratio ought to be quite different. Sometimes organisms, especially plants, do occur with double the normal number of chromosomes (and indeed can now be often made to occur by treatment with colchicine) ; and then these *tetraploids* (meaning " fourfolds ") as they are called, in opposition to the usual *diploids* (" twofolds ") do give rise to quite different Mendelian ratios after a cross, and these ratios are what would be expected from the random segregation of four members of one kind of chromosome instead of two.

It can also be prophesied (though the argument is too lengthy to give here) that the triploids, or plants with three of each kind of chromosome instead of two, which are produced when you cross a tetraploid with a diploid, will be wholly or largely sterile in sexual reproduction : and this also is confirmed by experiment.

The distance between different genes on the chromosome-maps I have mentioned is measured by the strength of linkage between them, and expressed in arbitrary " map-units " of distance. If gene A has been found to be say 20 units of distance away from gene B, and say five units away from gene C, then on the chromosome theory one can prophesy that the distance between genes B and C will be *either* 20 plus five, i.e. 25 units ; *or* 20 minus five, i.e. 15 units ; and experiment again confirms the prediction.

What are perhaps the most remarkable predictions only became possible later, with the discovery of the salivary gland chromosomes of Drosophila, the fruit-fly. Fruit-flies are ideal for genetic experiments, but their ordinary chromosomes are so unusually small as to be very unfavourable for microscopic study. Then one day it was discovered that in their salivary glands they contained giant chromosomes, so enormous that their fine structure can be seen under the microscope. This fine structure consists of a series of discs and bands, and each chromosome has a particular arrangement of these. Thus in addition to the theoretical maps of the genes deduced from linkage experiments, it was now possible to make actual maps of the bands and discs derived from observation. What is more, by brilliant but laborious experiments, it proved possible to equate the two, so that now in any textbook of genetics you will find maps which give not only the actual structure of the fruit-fly's chromosomes, but also the position of hundreds of genes known from breeding experiments.

(In a number of cases, indeed, it has been possible to define the precise limits of individual genes on the map, as well as their general position).

Now breeding experiments had occasionally given results which did not tally with the normal gene-map. Quite early, the Morgan school had put forward the hypothesis that these aberrant results were due to small sectors of a chromosome becoming misplaced—either reversed end to end, or detached from their normal position to become attached to other chromosomes. All the facts proved capable of being interpreted on this basis, but there were critics who felt that the suggested explanation was a bit far-fetched. However, with the discovery of the salivary gland chromosomes, it became possible to test the hypothesis, and it was a triumph for the chromosome theory when observation confirmed prophecy. When, for instance, the prophecy was that a piece of chromosome had been translocated elsewhere, lo and behold, that part of the salivary gland structure *was* found in the new place.

An even more spectacular confirmation happens with inversions (pieces of chromosome reversed end to end). It was previously known that at meiosis the members of a chromosome pair joined up with great exactitude, each gene pairing up with its opposite number. Now the only way that this could happen when a section of one chromosome is reversed would be for the section to form a twisted loop, fitting against an untwisted bulge of the normal chromosome. And this confor- mation is then visible through the microscope (and, I may add, never otherwise found).

Meanwhile a vast amount of patient work had served to establish two exceedingly important facts about Mendelism, using Mendelism in the extended sense to mean ' particulate chromosome inheritance '—inheritance by means of the transmission of definite particles or units of living substance, which are lodged in chromosomes, which maintain their identity from generation to generation, which segregate, and which can be recombined in various ways[1]. (The existence of particulate inheritance thus rules out all theories which assume that inheritance involves some enormous whole which is not separable into distinct units, and also all theories of " blending inheritance," i.e. the blending of hereditary material in sexual reproduction, whether the blending and dilution of wholes or of unit-particles).

The first fact was that Mendelism was not an exceptional phenomenon, but universal, at any rate in all but some of the lowest and simplest microscopic organisms. And the second was that it applies not only to obvious differences such as the difference between tall and dwarf peas or albino and coloured rabbits, but to all kinds of character-differences, whether large or small.

The second fact is the smallness of the differences which may mendelize ; this is very important. Thus one gene may act as a modifier of another, producing a slightly greater or smaller size, for instance, or a slightly darker or slightly lighter colour ; or two or more genes (" multiple genes ") may combine more or less equally in the production of some effect : and one character may be affected by a large number of these modifying and multiple genes.

The various genes can usually be disentangled by

[1] It now seems that a few properties are transmitted by so-called *plasmagenes*—units in the general protoplasm instead of in the chromosomes, which accordingly do not segregate and may be present in varying numbers in each cell ; but the great bulk of inheritance in the great majority of organisms is both particulate and chromosomal.

suitable (though often laborious) experiment. But the net effect they produce in nature is often one of continuous variation, such as a complete range of size from small to large, instead of discontinuous differences, such as that between Mendel's dwarf and tall peas.

One important point about particulate inheritance is that whenever a cross is made between two genetically different strains, and the F_1 offspring is capable of normal sexual reproduction, the F_2 will show a greater range of variation than the F_1. We already saw this with the cross between green and yellow peas, but the principle is of universal application, and often (as with the above mentioned cross between " yellow tall " and " green dwarf " peas) produces new types not seen in either parent or in the F_1.

This greater variation of F_2 would be impossible on any theory of blending inheritance, though it can be predicted as an inevitable result of particulate chromosomal inheritance. Sometimes so many pairs of genes are involved in a cross that it is impossible to disentangle them individually. But even then, if we find greater variation in F_2 than F_1, this is evidence of particulate chromosomal inheritance—i.e. of the differences between the two parents being due to genes in the chromosomes.

Many people have been puzzled by the wide differences, obviously of genetic nature, which can exist between the children of the same parents. Every one will know families where brothers or sisters differ strikingly from each other, as well as from either parent, in colouring, temperament, stature, intellectual ability, features, or body-build, and where environmental influence can be ruled out as insufficient to produce such large differences. However, such facts are the natural and inevitable consequence of Mendelian segregation and recombination, while they cannot be accounted for on the basis of any other theory of heredity.

The full significance of these facts can only be grasped after we have considered another set of facts recently established—the facts concerning mutation. Mutation is a term which has been given many meanings. However, it has now received a precise and scientific connotation, thanks to the work of neo-Mendelian genetics. It may perhaps be best defined, or rather best described, as the result of inexactitude in the process of self-reproduction by the material basis of heredity, the genes and chromosomes.

The genes possess the essential property of life, namely self-reproduction, or preferably self-copying (indeed, if we include plasmagenes, it is probable that they are the only elements in the organism which possess this property). At a certain stage in cell-growth, the string of genes becomes two strings, and one passes into each of the two daughter-cells. Every now and then, however, the copy is not quite exact, and then the new gene produces a different effect in development—absence versus presence of pigment, a different colour, a different hair-form, and so forth. It is by these new effects that mutations can be detected. Then breeding experiments will show whether the effect is due to a mutation in a gene, and not only that, but what particular gene has mutated. Even though a gene has mutated, it still retains the power of self-copying, so that the mutation is self-perpetuating—apart of course from further mutations which may affect it, either changing it back into its original form (" reverse mutation ") or into something new.

This inexact copying of genes is called gene-mutation. When large numbers of organisms are bred under controlled conditions, it is possible to tell when a new mutation occurs ; and this has been done with fruit-flies, maize, and a few other organisms. It turns out that for any particular gene mutation is a rare pheno-menon, though its frequency is different for different genes, as well as varying with conditions such as temperature ; that it may produce any degree of change, from death or gross disability, through marked effects like albinism or dwarfism, down to trifling quantitative differences ; that even when the differ-ences are trifling, they are always definite in extent—measurable steps of change ; that it is recurrent, in that the same kind of gene is subject to the same kinds of mutation, time after time ; that it is intensely local-ized, since although two genes of the same kind are always present in all normal cells, mutation never affects both, but only one ; and that it is a random process, in that mutations taken as a whole bear no functional or other relation to the needs of the organism or to the environment in which it finds itself.

All the mutations first studied were spontaneous—they just occurred, and occurred with equal frequency whether the cultures were subjected to special treatment or not. In 1927, however, H. J. Muller made the epoch-making discovery that mutations could be artificially produced by X-rays, and at a rate many times higher than spontaneous mutation. Later ex-periments (all again involving enormous numbers of facts) have shown that many kinds of radiations are effective in producing mutations, and also certain chemical agents such as mustard gas. In general, artificial mutations are similar to (and often identical with) spontaneous mutations, both in the effects they produce and in the fact that they are random.

I must also mention chromosome-mutations. These differ from gene-mutations in that they do not represent a change in the nature (presumably the chemical structure) of the gene, but quantitative additions or subtractions to or from the entire set of genes which make up the hereditary constitution. One kind of chromosome-mutation we have already referred to— the addition of entire sets of chromosomes and their contained genes. The most familiar is tetraploidy, the doubling of the whole outfit, providing four instead of two representatives of each kind of chromosome (and therefore of each kind of gene-unit). We also find the addition or subtraction of single whole chromosomes or of small bits of chromosomes ; and all these changes produce some effects on the characters of the organism

Gene-mutations, however, are the most important, for they provide the bulk of the building-blocks of evolutionary change. Once a gene has mutated, it goes on with its self-copying, so that a mutation can persist in the stock for a longer or shorter time. If the effects it produces are harmful, it will eventually be eliminated by natural selection ; if they are helpful, the possessors of the gene will be favoured by natural selection, so that the mutant gene will become more and more abundant in the species, and will eventually oust its " normal " parent, itself becoming normal for the stock. Recessive genes of many kinds, but each kind represented only in small numbers are always to be found in any species of animal and plant (apart from those which practise self-fertilization or close in-breeding, or have abandoned sexual reproduction for some asexual method). These must be the products of past mutation. Their frequency depends on the precise balance between their rate of elimination by natural selection on the one hand, and on the other, their " mutation-pressure," or the rate at which they are produced by new mutations—i.e. new failures of self-copying—in the " normal " genes of which they are the partners. If conditions change, they may become advantageous to the species and increase in number until they become ' normal ' ; or in some cases, two or more mutant genes, each by itself neutral or slightly deleterious, may in combination prove favourable. The stock of mutant genes carried in the chromosomes constitutes the evolutionary reserve of the organism.

Another very important fact is the following : that in general it is the small mutations, producing only slight effects, which are important in the life of the species and valuable for evolution.

On the basis of these facts, a general neo-Mendelian theory could now be framed, including the following main points :

(1) Almost all heritable differences between individuals " mendelize "—that is to say, their distribution in inheritance depends on the behaviour of the chromosomes, which contain the genes, which in their turn are the material units of heredity.

(2) All changes in the hereditary constitution are mutations—i.e. changes of definite extent ; these changes are usually within individual genes, but sometimes involve the addition or subtraction of whole genes or strings of genes, up to chromosomes and entire chromosome-sets. Thus all mendelizing differences between individuals—in other words, almost all the heritable variation of plants and animals—owe their origin to past mutation.

(3) Evolutionary change, whether large or small, is almost entirely due to the differential survival of mutant genes and their combinations, harmful ones being eliminated and useful ones being favoured and eventually becoming normal for the stock, through the automatic operation of natural selection. The material basis of evolution is thus the differential survival of genes and gene-complexes, and mutations are the quanta of evolutionary change.

(4) Mutations and the mendelizing effects they produce, though always definite in extent, may be very small, and these small mutations are the more important in evolution. As a result, the variation actually found in a species of animal or plant is generally continuous, without sharp breaks, even though it is based on discontinuous differences in the genes. (In the same sort of way, matter and energy appear continuous to us, although they are actually composed of discrete units— molecules, atoms and subatomic particles, together with energy-quanta ; e.g. the " uniform " pressure of a gas is the resultant of the very variable individual behaviour of all its myriad constituent unit-molecules).

The earlier mendelian geneticists, employing large mutations in their breeding experiments, had somewhat naively supposed that nature did the same in its gigantic experiment which we call evolution. They supposed that evolution proceeded by discontinuous jumps. It was natural for them to use sharply contrasting differences for this phase of their work, for these were much easier material with which to establish the mendelian laws and their general applicability. But they made the mistake of thinking that such differences were as important for their animal and plant possessors as for the human experimenters.

For meanwhile the facts of nature spoke in the opposite sense. For one thing, when large samples of animals or plants were measured, it was found that their variation, whether in size or shape or colour, was usually continuous, without trace of breaks or gaps. And for another, the fossil remains which were unearthed and investigated by palæontologists, showed that the actual course of evolution had been gradual too—no sudden transformations or leaps into a new type, but a slow and continuous process.

A violent controversy sprang up in the first decade of the 20th century between the Mendelian mutationists, headed by Bateson, who believed in discontinuity, and the anti-Mendelian biometricians, headed by Karl Pearson, who believed in continuity of variation and evolution. Further research showed, as so often, that both sides were right—up to a point. The Mendelians were right in believing that the material bases of inheritance and variation are particulate and discontinuous ; the biometricians were right in asserting that the variation and evolution actually exhibited by organisms is normally continuous. The two sets of facts could be reconciled when it was shown that the discontinuous quanta of change we call mutations are usually so small that their visible effects add up to apparent continuity.

Meanwhile mathematics had invaded genetics— a sure sign that the science was growing up. In the first place, the geneticist called on the theory of probability to give him greater certainty in his work. If you are breeding living animals and plants, especially the larger and slower-growing ones, you just cannot afford to raise large numbers of individuals, and often have to be content with a few score (although with small and rapidly breeding creatures like fruit-flies you can raise hundreds or even thousands : but then the labour of counting the different sorts individually under the microscope is portentous). In such a case, the distribution of characters may often depart widely from expectation, or may equally well be interpreted in different ways. Thus in a progeny of 20 a distribution of, say, 13 of one type to seven of another might equally well be a chance deviation from a 1 : 1 or from a 3 : 1 ratio. The calculus of probabilities enables the experimenter to apply tests to tell just how probable or improbable is any given difference between two figures, and so to say whether his results are " significant " or not. In this way he is able to say what exactly the odds are that a deviation from a theoretically expected ratio is accidental, or that an apparent effect produced by some experimental treatment is really due to the treatment or only to chance. In a similar way, if we were tossing pennies we could calculate whether a deviation from the expected 50 : 50 ratio of heads and tails was accidental, due to mere chance, or whether we should have to look for some other cause, such as the coins being weighted. Exactly similar methods have to be applied in the physical sciences when dealing with moderate numbers.

The development of genetics also led to the development of special methods and scientific precautions needed for research in the subject. Thus it speedily became clear that purity of material was just as important for genetical as for chemical experiment, since a gene can produce different effects according to the other genes with which it is associated. Inbreeding will automatically increase genetic purity (homozygosity), and calculation then showed what sort of inbreeding, practised over how many generations, would give any required degree of purity. A " pure line," once established, will stay pure indefinitely (apart from rare mutations), in spite of Lysenko's assertions to the contrary. Since genes may have different effects in different conditions, the need for the careful regulation of the environment in which the experiments are to be carried out (e.g. the temperature) also became apparent. Today no geneticist can expect his work to be taken seriously unless he states what are the methods and the scientific precautions he has used.

The application of probability methods and " significance tests " provided the geneticists with an important technical tool to help him in his work. But mathematics can be applied to genetics in other and more substantial ways. For instance, if a mutation and a normal gene are both present in a stock, and the one has on the average a 1 per cent. advantage over the other in the struggle for existence (in the sense that for every 100 of the normals, 101 of the mutants, survive into the next generation) then we can calculate the rate at which the mutant gene will increase at the expense of the normal ; (as a matter of interest, it is, from the point of view of evolution, quite rapid.) Further we can show that this rate will be different according as to whether the mutant is dominant or recessive. In this way, it was possible to take the first steps towards a quantitative theory of evolutionary change based upon Mendelian foundations.

Most fundamental of all, R. A. Fisher was able to demonstrate that evolution would be impossible unless inheritance were particulate. With the amount of variation actually found in nature, blending inheritance such as Darwin postulated would not permit natural selection to establish new characters in animals and plants—the blending would dilute and swamp any new variation, which would always regress towards the old, so that novelty would be swamped ; with blending inheritance, one could only expect evolution to occur if the amount and rate of new variation (mutation) were many times as high as what is actually found.

Thanks to the application of mathematical reasoning to Mendelian facts, not only is a general selectionist theory of evolution taking shape, but various particular deductions or prophecies can be made, which can then be tested by observation or experiment. For instance, it can be deduced that two sharply distinct forms cannot coexist in the same species (a condition known technically as dimorphism) unless there is a selective balance between them.[1]

The most spectacular example is that of melanism (the existence of a black or heavily pigmented form) in moths. Dominant melanism is found as a rare aberration in a great many moths, and is due to a dominant mutation in a single gene. However, in a number of species in western Europe, the dark melanic form has during the past hundred years become the only or far the commonest one in industrial areas, while in other parts of their range it is exceptional. Ford has now shown that this is due to a balance of selective advantage. The melanic has the advantage of being hardier and more resistant to all kinds of unfavourable conditions ; the " normal " lighter form has the advantage of escaping its enemies by being protectively coloured. The extra hardiness of the melanic is quite

[1] Sexual dimorphism is a special case in that in the higher animals a special genetic mechanism has been evolved in the chromosomes to produce an approximate equality of males and females.

large—in one experiment in which equal numbers of melanics and normals were expected, but where the brood was exposed to severely unfavourable conditions, only about half as many normals as melanics were able to survive to maturity.

If the light type had no counteracting advantage, the species would become all melanic, apart from rare aberrant light forms, in a few generations. Yet in the normal environment of the countryside, the selective advantage of protective colouration enjoyed by the light form is so great that the melanics are—or were—rare collector's prizes. In industrial towns, on the other hand, many of the normal enemies are absent ; probably the prevailing soot makes the dark form less conspicuous, the pale form more so, to what enemies are left ; and quite possibly the general conditions are more severe, so putting an extra premium on the melanic's greater hardiness.

Here is proof of the existence and efficacy of selection-pressure in nature, and of its acting on a Mendelian basis, to favour one or other of two competing genes. As a practical advantage arising from such deductions we may take the success of inbred corn (maize) in the United States. East and Jones deduced, by reasoning from Mendelian premisses, that close in-breeding for a certain considerable number of generations, followed by intercrossing the inbred lines, would give a fine strain, and one free from the common vice of ordinary maize strains, of constantly turning up a proportion of useless or unhealthy plants. They prophesied that each separate inbred line would be wretched, but that their subsequent intercrossing would restore their vigour and their size. All this came true, and in spite of the denunciation of inbreeding by the Michurinists, the most successful maize strains now used in the U.S.A. are the result of this application of mathematics to Mendelian fact, and there has been a marked increase of yield. (see pp. 96, 181).

Another mathematical method, of partial correlation, is now beginning to be applied in genetics, especially in the U.S.A., and especially in animal breeding, where large size and lengthy life-span, together with the great number of genes involved in producing any desirable character, make straightforward Mendelian analysis and synthesis practically impossible. It is unfortunate that the dispute between the biometricians and the Mendelians broke out when it did, in the very early stages of modern genetics. For while the mathematical techniques of Karl Pearson and his followers were obviously irrelevant to the study of the inheritance of the large, simple and sharply contrasted differences used by the early Mendelians, they can be adapted to deal with situations involving complex character-differences and continuous visible variation. All that is necessary is that they should be applied within a Mendelian framework of ideas, and not one involving blending inheritance or continuity of genetic variation. Biometric methods applied to neo-Mendelian postulates : here we have the reconciliation of the two opposites in this particular dispute, and also the possibility of much more rapid practical advance in practical breeding.

I must now pass from genetics in the narrow sense to evolution. Since Darwin's time there have been two main conflicting hypotheses concerning the method of evolution. One is based on the automatic natural selection of heritable variations which are already given, the other on the cumulative inheritance of acquired characters—changes in the organism imposed by changed environment or changed habits. Although Darwin (with a caution which in man's then state of complete ignorance of the mechanism and physical basis of heredity was probably justified) [1] ascribed some validity to both, yet the fact that to him alone goes the real priority for the epoch-making idea of natural selection, and that he regarded it as of considerably greater importance than the other, allows us to call the pure selectionist theory Darwinism. However, it is better to call it neo-Darwinism, since for one thing it represents a modification of Darwin's original views and for another Lysenko and his school still call themselves " Darwinians," and indeed claim to have incorporated all that is of value in Darwin's ideas.

The alternative hypothesis is usually known as Lamarckism, after its first proponent, although the ideas underlying its later variants are sometimes very different from those of Lamarck himself ; and the anti-Mendelians in the U.S.S.R., because of this and also for patriotic reasons, prefer to speak of Michurinism. In what follows I shall use the term neo-Lamarckism to cover all modern theories based on the idea of the inheritance of acquired characters, reserving Michurinism where need be for Lysenko's views.

Commonsense would probably say that both theories might be partially true, so that both mechanisms might contribute something to evolution. This was Darwin's

[1] In 1859, not even the elementary facts concerning reproduction were know. Pasteur's work had not yet killed the idea that life could be " spontaneously generated " ; it was not known that reproduction always involved the detachment of one or more living cells from the parent to form the offspring, nor that sexual reproduction always involved the fusion of the nuclei of two living cells; and chromosomes had not even been detected under the microscope.

own position, and the Michurinites, although ascribing greater weight to the Lamarckian factor, believe that selection is also important.

Since Darwin's time, facts (again in great numbers) have emerged which bear on the question. The most direct bearing, of course, is given by experiment ; but the body of our knowledge about the mechanism of heredity turns out to have a marked bearing on the common-sense view that both theories might be partially true ; and finally many facts of observation appear to be incompatible with Lamarckism but not with neo-Darwinism.

Let me mention three examples of this last type. The first is that of worker ants, bees, and wasps. These are neuter ; they cannot therefore pass on any modifications due to environment or way of life to their offspring, for they have no offspring. Yet they show the most striking adaptations to their way of life and their environment.

It has been objected that a few rare workers may become fertile and leave offspring : but these are so few that any large-scale Lamarckian inheritance through them is out of the question, and in any case the offspring produced are females (" queens "), whose characters differ from those of the neuter workers. Furthermore, the social insects are only a special case : for higher insects as a whole constitute a second and apparently insuperable obstacle to Lamarckism. After a larval life as a grub or nymph, they finally emerge in the perfect winged form—fly, wasp, dragonfly, beetle, butterfly or what not ; and after that they neither grow nor moult any more. What is more, their structure and their obvious and often marvellous adaptations are almost entirely determined by their exoskeleton or outer framework of the stiff horny material called chitin ; and this is secreted as so much non-living matter, and cannot be changed (as can our bones, within limits) by exercise or by outer influences. Thus it is physically impossible to imagine any way in which environment or way of life could modify the outer structure or form of a higher insect, since this depends on dead unmodifiable chitin, and further is given once and for all, as soon as the adult insect emerges from its last moult ; and if there are no modifications to transmit, they cannot very well be accumulated in evolution.

The third example is similar, and comes from ourselves and our vertebrate relatives. The only modification which use can effect in our teeth is to wear them down. It is therefore impossible that the structure of teeth, which is often obviously adapted to the work they have to do (think of the difference between the molars of a horse and a lion) could owe anything to Lamarckian inheritance.

Facts such as these show that Lamarckism is unnecessary, and certainly does not always operate, since extremely complex adaptations have arisen where there are no acquired characters to be inherited, or where no inheritance of them would be possible if they existed.

The facts concerning the mechanism of heredity have a slightly different bearing. They make it exceedingly difficult for us to believe in Lamarckian inheritance in any higher animal or plant. In the next few decades after Darwin's Origin of Species, the nature of sexual reproduction was elucidated for the first time. It was shown that it consisted in the transmission of actual living substance from parents to offspring. The living substance is that of two cells, or units of living matter, the egg and the sperm, one from the female, the other from the male parent. These unite, and their substance is combined in a single cell, the fertilized egg. This in turn is the first stage of the new life, or rather of the new individual or cycle of life, and gives rise by repeated division to all the cells of the new organism, both those of its individual body, or *soma*, and those of its so-called *germ-plasm*, or reproductive tissues (germ-cells) via the ovaries and testes. The new eggs or sperms which it produces receive no contributions from the cells of its muscles or brain or liver or any other organ of its body or soma : they originate by an unbroken chain of cell-division from the fertilized egg.[1]

These facts have been vividly expressed by saying that the individual is not really the parent of his or her or its offspring, but the uncle. This has been ridiculed by Lysenko as contrary to reason and common-sense ; but it is, biologically speaking, perfectly true ; for there is no direct transmission to offspring-body, from parent-body as a whole, though both are descended from a common " grandparent," the fertilized egg which gave rise both to parent-body and to parent-germplasm (see footnote).

Meanwhile the chromosomes in the nuclei of the cells were discovered, and it soon became obvious that they must be of some special importance, since they are constant in number for a given species, and since they are so accurately divided along their length at each cell-division, and the halves so accurately distributed

[1] Sometimes only the chromosome-containing nuclei of the cells unite, and sometimes the male cell contributes only its nucleus to the fertilized egg ; but the principle remains that the hereditary contributions of male and female parents are similar, and that there is continuity of living substance from both parents to the offspring.

to the daughter cells. It looked as if they must contain something important, with a very precise structure, strung out along their length, and qualitatively different in different regions. As we have seen, this is in fact true, though it was not proved until the best part of half a century had elapsed : they contain the string of genes which constitute the physical basis of heredity.

Furthermore, a distinguishing feature of sexual as against asexual reproduction is that it involves a prior halving of the normal number of chromosomes, so that the egg and sperm contain only this half number, and the normal number is made up one more by their union. As the offspring inherits equally from both parents, and as the chromosomes are the only contribution which is equal in both parents, it was natural to equate the chromosomes with the germ-plasm. And this also is in essence true.

Weismann, in the early 1890's perceived all this in general terms, although some of his detailed hypotheses turned out to be unfounded, specially as to the structure and function of chromosomes. But he grasped the main implication of the new facts—namely that if life is transmitted by continuity of substance, and that continuity is assured by cell-division (plus one act of cell-fusion between egg and sperm), it is exceedingly difficult to see how any changes in the individual body or soma can affect the reproductive cells or germ-plasm—in other words how any kind of Lamarckian inheritance could possibly operate.

It would of course be possible to imagine changes in the body having some general or non-specific effect on the germ-plasm. But the essence of Lamarckism is that detailed adaptive adjustments of the body and its organs to changed environment or way of life are supposed to be able to produce corresponding changes, though of less extent, in the offspring, and to produce them even in the absence of the influences which originally caused the bodily changes in the parent. Thus, Lamarck himself suggested that when a land bird took to the water, the act of swimming stimulated the growth of a web between its toes, and that this webbing was gradually accumulated by heredity. But, once the facts concerning reproduction were discovered, to suppose that a change in the skin of a bird's toes could influence the genes (or indeed any other conceivable mechanism of heredity) in the bird's egg in such a way that the egg gave rise to a new bird with a little more webbing, is like supposing that a telegram sent off from Pekin in Chinese will arrive in London already translated into English.

Weismann undoubtedly exaggerated the sharpness of the distinction between soma and germ-plasm, and the impossibility of any influence from the former acting on the latter ; but he did, once and for all, make clear the extreme improbability of Lamarckism in the ordinary sense.[1] Furthermore, all later discoveries have merely served to make the improbability even greater. The genes have been shown to possess a quite extraordinary stability in the face of almost all

[1] In man and higher animals, germ-cells are never produced from any functioning tissue of the soma. Even in higher plants, where reproductive cells can arise from the soma, it is only from one tissue of the soma (the subepidermal layer) that they so arise. There is still a continuity of reproduction through one set of cells, not through others, and there is still no conceivable mechanism by which other parts of the soma could contribute to the germ-plasm, or by which changes in other tissues could affect the reproductive cells. The germ-plasm, in the shape of the chromosomes, runs in a single line of self-reproducing substance from fertilized egg to gamete, and its self-reproduction is exceedingly accurate.

kinds of external influences, while their occasional instability as revealed by their mutation points in the opposite direction to that demanded by Lamarckism, since the variations thus produced are unrelated to the environment or the way of life of their possessors. In any case, any Lamarckian theory whatsoever must come to terms with the facts concerning the physical basis of heredity. (I should have said must come to *scientific* terms with them. For of course if the issue is to be decided on other than scientific grounds, the facts can just be dismissed, as Lysenko and the Academy of Sciences have recently done. But this, though it may be a political victory, is a scientific defeat).

There remain the actual experiments concerning the heritability of acquired characters. Many of these have given wholly negative results. For instance, breeding fruit-flies in total darkness for over 60 generations (a period equivalent to some 2,000 years on the human time-scale) had not the slightest effect on their visual capactities ; this was the reverse of encouraging to the Lamarckian upholders of the evolutionary effects of use and disuse, who had claimed that the degeneration of the eyes to be found in cave animals was directly produced by the cumulative effects of their disuse, in the darkness of the caves, over a number of generations.

A more general negative answer was given by the many experiments involving pure lines. A pure line is a strain which is genetically uniform, either because it reproduces asexually or because it has been rendered uniform by close inbreeding, including that closest form of inbreeding, self-fertilization. A pure line, like any other set of organisms, will grow up differently in different conditions ; but put it back in standard conditions, and it will give the same standard result which it gave originally. The modifications due to changed environment have *not* been inherited, even to the slightest extent.

However, a number of experimenters have claimed positive results—for instance Kammerer with the mode of reproduction of his amphibians and McDougall with the learning capacity of his rats. But without exception, repetition of such experiments by others has failed to confirm the claims. Sometimes the original experimenter had failed to take proper scientific safeguards, and in one or two regrettable cases there had been fraud or the suspicion of fraud.

One particular instance is interesting, because at first sight it seemed to show how a change in conditions might affect the germ-plasm, and affect it in a way that was related to the original changed conditions. Guyer and Smith claimed that injecting rabbits with a serum containing an antibody against rabbit lens, caused the appearance in later generations of young rabbits with congenitally defective lenses in their eyes. Since the antibody destroys lens protein, this would be intelligible if one or more of the genes responsible for building up the lens contained the same protein as that found in the lens. Several biologists have repeated the experiment, but have obtained only negative results. On the other hand, Sturtevant (1944) records that Hyde in the U.S.A. in 1940 told Sturtevant that he was getting some confirmatory evidence of the reality of the effect. Unfortunately, he died before the experiments were concluded.

As Sturtevant has pointed out, however, even if Guyer and Smith's findings are confirmed, this would not be Lamarckism in the proper sense. It would depend on the fact that a gene was producing in the body substances chemically similar to itself. It is possible that this holds in some other cases of immunological reactions, e.g. for some genes responsible for the production of particular antigens in our own red blood-corpuscles.

There are also many possible sources of error in such experiments. As I have pointed out in the preceding chapter, one such source of error, which seems definitely to have been at work in Lysenko's own experiments, is the use of genetically impure strains of animals and plants. It is still possible, for instance, that Guyer and Smith's results may have been due to some of his original animals having contained recessive genes causing lens defects (which we know do exist in rabbits). Another possible source of error is unconscious selection by the experimenter, which may *simulate* the inheritance of acquired characters.

If a plant strain, for instance, is grown under new conditions, it will usually show some adaptation to the conditions—becoming more fleshy, for instance, in a salty environment, or more luxuriant and green in nitrogen-rich conditions. It is natural to take as the parents of the next generation those which react most strongly to the treatment. But, unless the strain is absolutely pure, these are quite likely to be genetically different from the average, and different precisely in being better adapted to the new conditions or in being able to react more strongly to them. Such a process of unconscious selection continued over quite a few generations will give a strain with permanently new adaptive characteristics—but this will be merely a simulation of Lamarckism : it will not be due to any inheritance of acquired characters, but to selection from among innate characters (or rather the genes responsible for them) which were already in existence before the experiment started.

Such a false simulation of a Lamarckian effect need not be due, even unconsciously, to selection on the part of the experimenter : the selection may sometimes be entirely automatic, as is natural selection in wild species. Thus domesticated turkeys turned out in the wild become wilder in disposition in a few generations, while wild turkeys brought into captivity grow tamer; and in both cases this has been proved to be due to the elimination of birds whose temperament unfits them for the radically altered new environment to which they are subjected (Leopold, 1944).

The only way to guard against these sources of error through selection, is to use strains of as high a degree of genetic purity as possible. And to obtain such strains, whether from ordinary commercial breeds or from ordinary wild populations, requires over ten generations of close inbreeding.

In any case, the record of the past 80 years of work on this subject is quite definite. Although positive claims have been repeatedly made, not one has stood the test of repetition or critical analysis.

In parenthesis, it is very fortunate for the human species that acquired characters are *not* readily impressed on the hereditary constitution. For if they were, the conditions of dirt, disease and malnutrition in which the majority of mankind have lived for thousands of years would have produced a disastrous effect upon the race.

Two general points remain to be mentioned. The first is the self-contradictory character of classical Lamarckism, which assumed that any and every new effect of the environment or of use and disuse could be inherited. If this were so, we should have the following sequence of events. (1) An organism living for a very long period in certain environmental conditions, and therefore having the modifications due to those conditions impressed upon its heredity. (2) The same organism exposed to new and different environmental conditions (e.g. partial vernalization treatment) for a much shorter period, and having the modifications due to those new conditions impressed on its heredity. (3) The organism capable of reproducing the newly-inherited characters in spite of the absence of the conditions which brought them about. But, as Ray Lankester pointed out many years ago, this implies that the effects of the longer period of exposure are weaker than those of the shorter.

It is fair to add that this theoretical contradiction does not apply to Lysenko's Michurinism, which postulates that Lamarckian effects only take place when the heredity is " shattered " or " shaken," but can then be expected to be relatively permanent. (But it is also well to remind ourselves that the shattering or shaking of the hereditary constitution is neither an established fact nor easily reconciled with various facts that are established).

The second point is R. A. Fisher's demonstration (see discussion in Huxley, 1942) that the inheritance of acquired characters could not lead to evolutionary change unless it were far stronger and more complete than any of its proponents have dreamt of suggesting. If it is slight, it will be swamped and overridden by the degree of selection we know to exist. If, on the other hand, it were strong enough to override selection, it would be readily detectable by simple experiments, and this is not the case.

We may sum up by saying that the theoretical difficulties in the way of any inheritance of acquired characters are enormous, and that those in the way of its being effective in evolution are overwhelming ; that no such inheritance has ever been proved to exist, and that none of the numerous claims to have produced a Lamarckian effect have stood the tests of criticism and repetition. Samuel Butler, Bernard Shaw, and Lysenko may assert that evolution without the inheritance of acquired characters is unthinkable : but the facts proclaim the contrary.

Another set of facts concerns the relation between genetics and individual development. Opponents of Mendelism have asked how it is possible for each of the thousands of tiny details of structure and adaptation to be looked after by a separate gene, and how the right mutations happened at the right moment in all these genes so as to co-ordinate their actions. The answer is simple : they aren't, and they don't. Although there are plenty of examples of genes having a detailed or localised effect, yet in a great many cases they do not or need not do so, because the development of the individual from egg to adult operates through the mechanism of broad patterns. I will give a few examples. It is a well known fact of observation, that certain organs of mammals, notably such appendages as horns and antlers, but also, though to a lesser degree, the extremities in general, usually increased in their *relative* size as the absolute size of the whole body goes up ; other organs, on the other hand, such as the brain, decrease in relative size with increase of absolute size.

Analysis has shown that it is not necessary to postulate two different genes or sets of genes controlling the relative size of such organs and the absolute size of the body separately : the increase or decrease of relative size with increase of absolute size is the automatic result of a law or pattern of growth (which we do not fully understand, but must accept as a fact). Special genes may come in to change the rate of the process or affects its details, but the process itself is unitary.

With antlers, a further concomitant of greater size is greater complication—in general, larger antlers have a more elaborate structure, with more ' points.' This again is in essence automatic : a separate set of genes for each new point is not required, for the antler is of such a nature that the bigger it grows, the more it branches.

An even more striking case is that of the detailed adaptations of our tendons and sinews. As already pointed out in a previous chapter, these do not demand a large number of separate genes, but arise automatically in the course of development. They are adaptive modifications, but they are acquired anew in each generation, and are not inherited.

If we look at the situation historically, we can say that Lamarckism has been by-passed by the development of genetical science. Just as Darwin's hypothesis of pangenesis or the Michurinist hypothesis of heredity being a function of the whole organism have been rendered out-of-date and untenable by the discovery of the physical basis of heredity in the chromosomes, so the Lamarckian hypothesis of ⋅ the inheritance of acquired characters has been rendered out-of-date and untenable by the discovery of the physical basis of evolution, in the natural selection and consequent differential survival of mutant genes.

The Lamarckians and Michurinists are right in stressing that there is a relation between environment and the adaptive characters of the organisms. But they are wrong in supposing that the relation is simple and direct. It is complex and indirect : mutations are essentially random, and selection preserves those few which happen to be favourable in the particular environment. This is a statement of scientific fact, which no a priori considerations can alter.

A word must be said about our new knowledge concerning evolution as a process. [1]

Let us remember that in Darwin's time next to nothing was known concerning the actual course of evolution. Men knew that in general more complicated creatures tended to appear in the later-deposited layers of the earth's crust, and that was all. To-day, however, the accumulation of many thousands of facts—in the shape of fossil specimens from geological horizons of known date—have enabled us to reconstruct, often in great detail, the past history of many group of animals, from horses and elephants to sea-urchins and fish of various kinds.

From this picture one fact stands out clearly—that one of the main features of evolution is the existence of long-term trends, extending for periods to be measured in tens of millions of years (but not in hundreds of millions nor yet in hundreds of thousands) ; and each of these trends is what is technically called a specialization, which means a steady but one-sided progress in the direction of greater adaptation towards

[1] For details, I must refer my readers to my *Evolution, the Modern Synthesis*, (London and New York, 1942), also to such books as E. Mayr's *Systematics and the Origin of Species* (1942), T. Dobzhansky's *Genetics and the Origin of Species* (1941), D. Lack's *Darwin's Finches* (1947), and H. B. Cott's *Adaptive Coloration in Animals* (1940).

a particular way of life. The horse stock is the classical material for demonstrating specialization, as the fruit-fly is the classical material for demonstrating the method of inheritance. The specialization of the horse, which took at least 40 million years, adapted the stock to life on plains. The progressive adaptation of the limbs and feet to swift running and of the teeth to a grass diet is extremely striking.

Each such specialization eventually comes to an end, in the sense that there is no further major improvement in its particular adaptations : thus there has been no major change in the horse stock for at least five million years.

These facts can be readily explained on neo-Darwinian lines, on the basis of neo-Mendelism plus natural selection ; the selection of useful genes inevitably pushes the stock at a steady rate along the path of adaptation, but only until such time that further advance would be useless or harmful (a horse cannot reduce the number of toes below one per foot, nor profitably increase the complexity of pattern of its molar teeth, which serve as mill-stones for grinding hard grass-stems, beyond the fineness it has now realised). Per contra, the facts are less readily explicable on any other theory of evolution.

Furthermore, if these long-term general adaptations of an entire group to a general way of life can be most readily interpreted on a neo-Darwinian basis, the same holds true for the more specific phenomena to which the term adaptation is often, though incorrectly, restricted—such phenomena as the cryptic coloration (" protective resemblance ") of so many animals, or the arrangements for securing cross-fertilization in many flowering plants. There was a time when it was

biologically unfashionable to pay too much attention
to such detailed adaptations or to believe too much in
their value to their possessor. However, the intensive
studies of the last few decades have shown that adaptation, often of the most delicate and complex nature, is
all-pervading in organic life, while at the same time
the development of neo-Darwinism has shown that
natural selection not only can but *must* produce
adaptations. In fact we can now turn the tables on
objectors by saying that the more extraordinary and
apparently incredible an adaptation is, the more it
demonstrates the power of natural selection.

I now pass to the subject of systematics, or the detailed
description and classification of animals and plants.
This is a branch of biology which at one time seemed
in danger of being overwhelmed by the mere mass of
the detailed facts it had accumulated. However, in
the past 25 years or so, various general principles have
emerged which have materially changed the position,
by providing a framework of ideas strong enough to
carry the bulk of the facts.[1] Taking birds as the group
whose systematics has been most thoroughly investigated, we find, for example, that they have been
diversified into thousands of species, or groups which do
not normally interbreed, but that within these groups
two further kinds of diversification are often to be
found. The first is their frequent subdivision into
subspecies—groups which differ slightly from each
other, but are still capable of interbreeding, and
occupying different geographical areas. The second is
the frequent existence of so-called *clines*, or gradients
of some character, apparently adaptive in nature, such
as size or shape or coloration, trending more or less

[1] See E. Mayr, *Systematics and the Origin of Species*, New York, 1942.

uniformly across the area occupied by a species or subspecies.

Another general principle or law is that geographical or other isolation favours diversification, so that for instance the same general type of land animal will have evolved into many more species and subspecies on a group of islands than on a corresponding area of the mainland.

All these facts, again, can be interpreted on a neo-Mendelian, neo-Darwinian basis ; and some—such as the existence of zones of relatively high variability where the ranges of two subspecies meet, or the extreme diversification, sometimes apparently not adaptive, which may occur in very small populations when they are geographically isolated,—are difficult or impossible to explain on a Lamarckian or indeed any non-Mendelian basis.

Finally, when subspecies or species are fully or reasonably fertile when experimentally crossed, the results are either obviously Mendelian, or interpretable on a Mendelian basis ; and similar results hold for the species-crosses which occasionally occur in nature.

All these facts, laws, principles, and theories can now be built up into a single system—modern evolutionary biology—within a single comprehensive framework of ideas—neo-Darwinism. In a similar way, there now exists a single system covering modern physics (and indeed extending far into the originally separate domain of chemistry) with a single theoretical framework, that of atomic physics. There is a difference, in that the process has taken place more recently in biology, so that the theoretical framework is not so completely consolidated as in physics, and its general acceptance by scientists not so universal. However, the essence of the situation is the same, in that evolutionary biology has attained the status of a unified branch of science, underlain by a single general theory which is not only capable of interpreting the facts of the science in a broad way, but is quantitative, and has predictive value. In other words, evolutionary biology has, scientifically speaking, come of age.

I will try to recapitulate the present position, but from the vantage-point of this new maturity of our science. Neo-Mendelism has shown that there is a material basis for inheritance, and that the enormously great bulk of this is particulate, consisting of the units called genes, which exist in single rows or chains within the chromosomes. The genes possess the essential property of life, in that they are self-copying. But the self-copying is not always exact : inexact self-copying occasionally occurs and produces mutations. These still possess the properties of self-copying and further mutations. The mutations are random, or we had better say undirected, in the sense that they occur in many directions, and that they are not adaptively related either to the environment or to the general evolutionary direction being pursued by the stock, or to the agencies which have produced them. Some of them, indeed, seem to be entirely due to chance, in being due to spontaneous rearrangements of subatomic structure.

The phenomena of inheritance over a few generations also follow from the nature of the chromosome machinery and the way its elements are distributed at sexual reproduction.

The phenomena of evolution—that is to say of change of inherited character over many generations—all follow from the above facts concerning the material basis of inheritance. In the first place, natural selection automatically comes into operation. Any mutant gene renders its possessors slightly different in regard to their average ability to survive and reproduce—in other words, increases or decreases their advantage in what Darwin called the struggle for existence, so that a gene conferring advantage will become slightly more frequent in the species in each generation. Mathematical calculation has demonstrated that quite a small advantage will lead, in what is biologically a quite reasonable time, to the virtual or total replacement of the old gene by its new mutant representative.

Self-copying leads to reproduction, and reproduction makes it inevitable that there should be a struggle for existence, for it always tends to produce more offspring than can survive : and incomplete copying or mutation, by introducing differences among the competing individuals, makes it inevitable that the struggle for existence should result in differential survival of differently endowed types.

This will occur even with a sexual reproduction. However, when sexual reproduction occurs, as it does in the great majority of organisms, the mechanism of heredity is such that it allows the recombination of characters (Mendel's Second Law, together with the laws of partial linkage). This means that any mutant genes, whether newly produced or present in the constitution as the result of mutation at an earlier period, can be combined with each other and with old, unmutated genes to produce quite new combinations of characters. These combinations are often much more favourable than any single mutation, so that sexual reproduction permits both greater speed and greater flexibility of evolution.

A general mathematical theory of selection is possible on these bases, and enables us to explain or even to make prophecies concerning the various phenomena of evolution, such as adaptation, long-term specialization, all-round progressive evolution, the origin of species and sub-species, and many others.

Self-reproduction, mutation, and sexual recombination result in Mendelian inheritance on the one hand, and natural selection on the other : and natural selection, when operating on animals and plants which show particulate inheritance of a Mendelian type, leads to evolutionary change, including both the progressive advance and the diversification of life.

All these facts, processes, and ideas are now firmly linked with each other to form a single whole. It is important to realize that neo-Darwinism now includes neo-Mendelism.[1] It means evolution produced by natural selection operating in a Mendelian world of life. It is also important to realize that neo-Darwinism in this extended sense forms a coherent whole, in which theory and fact are inextricably combined. In Darwin's time, natural selection was " only a theory." Now it is a fact—we know that selection (differential survival) exists in nature, we know the genetic and reproductive mechanisms through which it operates, and we can measure the resultant selection-pressure.

Finally, I would like to make brief mention of another set of facts, concerning the chemical constitu-

[1] As one would expect, neo-Mendelian genetics has reached a higher level of scientific development than neo-Darwinian evolutionary theory. In genetics we can make detailed prophecies and can often account scientifically for all the details of a particular phenomenon. In evolution, where situations are more complicated, and experiment is rarely possible, we can give general scientific interpretations and occasionally make rather general prophecies ; but it will take time before we are in a position to account fully for all the details of any particular evolutionary situation.

tion and structure of the chromosomes. Of recent
years, various elaborate physical methods such as
spectrography under the microscope, X-ray analysis,
etc. have enabled us to make a beginning in this
difficult field. It is still only a beginning, but certain
interesting facts are now established, and interesting
probabilities opening up for investigation. These may
be summed up for our purpose by saying that a normal
gene consists primarily of a particular kind of protein,
attached in some way to the neighbouring genes at
its either end. The protein of genes is linked with
nucleic acid, which becomes attached to and detached
from the protein in a regular cycle. Both nucleic acid
and protein are indispensable constituents of genes
(including plasmagenes).

The protein is in the form of an elongated chain of
groups of atoms (polypeptide chain), and the molecules
of nucleic acid seem to be fitted on to this chain rather
as the steps of a spiral staircase are fitted on to the
central column.

Recently Pease and Baker (1949) by special techniques, have been able to see, with the aid of the electron
microscope, what are almost certainly actual genes.
In any case they have discovered small objects inside
the chromosomes, about the size of an average virus or
bacteriophage, of various shapes (leaf-like, spheroidal,
and cigar-shaped), and composed of nucleic acid and
protein.

Proteins are of course the most complicated of all the
chemical constituents of living bodies, a single protein
molecule sometimes containing many hundreds of
atoms. Through slight variations in the position and
number of the different kinds of atoms and atom-
groupings, an almost infinite number of specifically

different kinds of protein can be produced, each with its own particular chemical properties. The protein molecules of genes appear to be particularly large and complex, so that each gene presumably has its main framework composed of one particular kind of protein (or, possibly, a few particular kinds) : it is this difference in protein structure which confers their specificity on genes, and makes every kind of gene different from every other.

It seems probable that the combination of nucleic acid with a very complex kind of protein confers on the gene the capacity for self-reproduction or self-copying. The gene gets its specificity from the protein, while the nucleic acid seems to be responsible for various aspects of the behaviour of the chromosomes such as their spiral coiling at certain times. Mutation would then be due to minor rearrangements in the structure or composition of a particular kind of protein molecule.

In any case, the facts, though still rudimentary, are important as taking our knowledge of the physical basis of heredity down below the microscopic level to the chemical level, and making it correspondingly more difficult to believe in a " heredity " or hereditary constitution diffused through every part of the organism, as the Michurinites want us to believe.

This sketch of the development of genetics is of necessity extremely brief and incomplete. However, it will, I hope, have shown that genetics to-day is not just some scattered facts with a few speculative ideas superimposed, but a large, flourishing, and coherent science, whose chief achievement is to have demonstrated that heredity is particulate and in the main chromosomal—in other words neo-Mendelian.

It is still actively developing, and making incursions into new territories. In this frontier region of research, many questions are still unsettled ; but behind this advancing front there is a large settled area of established knowledge. That knowledge cannot simply be rejected : it is now part of our human heritage. To reject it on ideological grounds, as Lysenko and the Academy of Sciences and the Communist Party of the U.S.S.R. have attempted to do, is scientifically illegitimate and a betrayal of the human intellect.

CHAPTER 5

THE TOTALITARIAN REGIMENTATION OF
THOUGHT

In previous chapters, I have tried to present in some detail the situation concerning genetical and evolutionary science in the U.S.S.R. This must be related to a larger picture—the situation of thought and expression in general. Under this head we have to include the whole range of intellectual and artistic activity, comprising natural and social science, philosophy, the humanities, law, economics, and creative expression in literature, the plastic arts and architecture and music.

In the U.S.S.R., as is now common knowledge, thought and expression have been to a greater or lesser extent compulsorily socialized—subordinated to an over-riding social philosophy and subjected to State (political) control, so that its freedom or autonomy is consciously and expressly restricted. It is, of course, obvious that thought and expression are nowhere completely autonomous, being always limited by their material, social, and spiritual or intellectual environment ; but this limitation is, in the western world of to-day, for the most part an automatic conditioning, not a conscious restriction, and is moderate in extent.

Fortunately, we have now at our disposal a valuable study, written in an objective spirit by acknowledged experts, of the general trends in the U.S.S.R. since the end of the war, and published in the Annals of the *American Academy of Political and Social Science* ([8]). After a general introduction, this deals with political and social life, including the post-war role of the Communist Party ; with economic life ; with cultural trends; and with foreign policy and international relations. I commend this study to my readers. Meanwhile, the following points arising from it, and from other sources, including my own experience as well as Alexander Werth (1949) and John Langdon-Davies (1949), appear to be relevant.

In what follows I am not concerned to be anti-Soviet or pro-Soviet: I am trying to present a statement of the present situation in the sphere of thought in the U.S.S.R., together with some suggestions as to the reasons which have led to that situation. If I criticize or condemn some of the methods used, that is not because I am hostile to the U.S.S.R. (it is one of the most disconcerting features of present Soviet mentality that criticism—even friendly or constructive criticism—is immediately interpreted as a sign of enmity) [1], but

[1] It is I think relevant to give an example of this violent reaction to criticism, drawn from my personal experience. At the World Congress of Intellectuals at Wroclaw in 1948, Taylor, a Fellow of Magdalen College, Oxford, protested against the atmosphere of hatred in which the discussions had started, and against the inaccurate belittlement of the western Allies' role in the war in general and of their aid to the U.S.S.R. in particular (a subject also mentioned by Barghoorn in[8], p. 2), and asked his hearers to consider the good as well as the bad elements in American culture and policy ; he urged that an attempt should be made to find a common platform for intellectuals throughout the world. Later, Hovde, the distinguished head of the New School for Social Research in New York, criticized the methods of the Congress in that it was not aimed at a reconciliation between Eastern and Western culture and ideology.

I myself made the same criticism, that mere denunciation was useless and undesirable, that reconciliation of the two opposites was desirable ; and that both sides should recognize the faults as well as the merits of their own system (citing as a fault in the Soviet system, the unfortunate results of enforced " socialist realism " in the arts). I also said that the Congress should try to find points of agreement, rather than assume disagreement from the outset ; and made many attempts to make the final Resolution less of an attack on the U.S.A. and more of an appeal for freedom and for constructive and co-operative effort.

because I believe that they are bad—bad in themselves, bad in their effects on human progress and
achievement, and in the long run bad for the
U.S.S.R.

I consider that the methods used by certain groups
and certain sections of the press in the U.S.A. to
denigrate the U.S.S.R. and to foment hatred of Communism are equally bad and equally regrettable. But
their discussion does not fall within the scope of this
book.

Central to the present state of affairs is the historical
fact that Soviet policy has undergone a radical change
since the war, apparently with a view to preparing the
people of the U.S.S.R. for a long struggle, possibly
involving war, with the capitalist world in general, and
the U.S.A. in particular.

To effect this, the revival of patriotic feeling for the
fatherland, " Holy Russia," which was deliberately
fostered during the war, with emphasis on Russian
history and the achievements of Russia as a nation, has

However, this is how the matter was reported by a Soviet writer,
in an article in *Soviet Literature* for November 12th, 1948 :—

" The overwhelming majority of the congress stood for unequivocal
denunciation of the imperialists who were striving for domination over
the world. However, imperialism had its advocates at the congress too
—very few of them, it is true. The Oxford historian, Mr. Taylor,
roused the angry protests of the congress delegates by attempting to
defend those for whom all the freedom-loving nations entertain a
justifiable loathing. He appealed to the delegates to believe in the non-
existent blessings coming from across the ocean and not to criticize the
expansion of American imperialism carried out under the guise
of "relief".

These appeals, however, were futile. The only ones who, to the
indignation of the whole congress, attempted to support the obscurantist
ideas of the Oxford speaker were Julian Huxley, the specious director
of Unesco, who, though he calls himself a scientist, is rather a zealous
servant trying to find favour in the eyes of his American masters, and an
" historian " from America by the name of Hovde whose behaviour
resembles that of an agent of the U.S. State Department rather than that
of a scientist."

been retained, but has been coupled with a glorification of communism and the present regime as the system under which alone the nation can successfully advance to new achievements. Nationalism and patriotism, Marxist theory and Stalinist practice, have been combined, with the deliberate and perfectly understandable intent of making Soviet society as monolithic, and the Soviet State as massively powerful, as possible. This synthesis is usually styled " Soviet patriotism " (Fainsod in [8], p. 25).

One factor involved in the adoption of this trend was the hostile reaction of the other Allies (and of the western world in general) to the U.S.S.R.'s policy of expansion or consolidation of its power, in eastern and central Europe after the close of hostilities, coupled with its expectation of obtaining enormous loans or credits from the U.S.A. and other capitalist countries. " When American opinion grasped the nature of the Soviet programme, angry disillusionment set in. When the Kremlin realized that its hopes might be dashed and its fears confirmed, it began, at first stealthily, to transfer the symbols of hostility and aggression from Nazi Germany to ' imperialist ' America." (Barghoorn, in [8], p. 1).

The tendency to denigrate the west, and especially the U.S.A., has since become accentuated. American policy, including cultural policy, is ascribed to the influence of " fascist warmongers," and any attempt by the U.S.A. to strengthen its economic or political position is referred to as an example of " American imperialism." The word *imperialism* is, of course, never mentioned in relation to the consolidation of Soviet power in eastern Europe.

In view of past history, from the time of Denikin to

that of Hitler, both the Kremlin's fears of capitalist countries, and its desire for security, are eminently understandable, whatever may be thought of the tactics employed. And in view of those fears and that desire, it was natural, and perhaps inevitable, that the Soviet authorities should have wished to develop a strong and unified national sentiment, unquestionably accepted, based on national pride, directed towards the future triumph of the system—at once both national and international—of Soviet Communism.

To achieve this, the Soviet authorities considered that it was necessary and desirable to mobilize and regiment not only public opinion in the ordinary sense, but all the higher activities of the mind, both intellectual and aesthetic, from natural science to art and music, from philosophy to literature and history. Thought and creative expression had to become a weapon of foreign policy and an instrument of domestic policy in the struggle of the Soviet State to survive and to achieve its aims in the difficult post-war world. With this in view, the attempt has been made to weld the mental activities of the people of the U.S.S.R.—their ideas and emotions, their intellects and their aspirations —into a monolithic whole, an instrument for the attainment of a definite but difficult goal.

I shall come back later to this question of the unification of thought in the U.S.S.R. into a single system of ideas. Here I must turn to a consideration of various separate subjects. We find that restriction has effected various fields to a different extent and in rather different ways.

In politics it of course operates through the one-party system, which allows freedom of political thought or expression only within the limits of communist party doctrine.

Since 1944, as described by Fainsod (in [8], p. 20f), the discipline of the party itself has been strengthened, and much attention has been given to the political and ideological education of its members. At the same time, widespread campaigns for the indoctrination and political training of the general population were undertaken. Great emphasis has been laid on specific communist doctrines such as the inevitability of a crisis rapidly supervening and bringing about the disintegration of capitalist economy, and the superiority of the Soviet system to all others—doctrines which have coloured much of Soviet policy and behaviour since the end of the war. It has vigorously condemned " apolitical " attitudes among members and non-members alike, and has insisted that intellectual activities should be " partisan."

As Fainsod writes, " its special mission is to reassert its control over all phases of national life." The Department of Propaganda and Agitation of the Central Committee of the Party was strengthened, and in 1946 began issuing the journal called *Culture and Life*, which exerted a very powerful effect in the campaign for the socialization of thought and expression to which this chapter is devoted. The energy with which Zhdanov prosecuted this campaign on behalf of the Central Committee is a reminder of the official communist view that all human activities have a political aspect, and should be carried on with a conscious recognition of their political implications.

In history and the social sciences, restriction is as severe, and perhaps even more productive of distortion (as an example of the distortion of history, I may cite the fact that in the Museum of the Revolution there is not—or was not in 1945 when I was in Moscow—any mention of the part played by Trotsky in the Revolution).

Yakobson (in [8], pp. 123-133) gives a detailed account of post-war historical research in the U.S.S.R. As he says, Pokrovsky's remark, " history is politics projected into the past," is still characteristic of the Soviet attitude towards historical research.

" Indicative of the power wielded by the changing dictates of the party line is the repeated reorganization of one of the principal Soviet historical periodicals . . . Each change has been a political act resulting from an important shift in policy decided on by the party." This periodical, founded in 1931 with the title *Class Warfare*, was rechristened *Historical Journal* in 1937, with no reason given except that it would from now on be edited " according to the directives of the party." The real reason was probably the necessity of soft-pedalling the theme of class warfare while the United Front policy was in favour.

Then, one month after VE day, in June 1945, " the subscribers to the journal were advised that its publication had been discontinued and that instead they would receive a new periodical entitled *Voprosy Istorii* (Historical Questions). The editorial board of the *Historical Journal* was declared to have neglected its duties, to have failed in carrying out its assignment, and to have lowered unpardonably the scholarly standard of the publication . . . The new magazine itself was intended primarily as ' a militant organ of the Marxist-Leninist historical school,' which was recognized as the only admissible school of historical thinking. It was given the task of fighting ' for the application of the principle of dialectical materialism to the analysis of the historical past.' Once more the emphasis was placed on class warfare."

In 1946, the Academy of Sciences enjoined its various sections to work out five-year plans for their respective disciplines. However, when the historians presented their plan for Party approval, it met with disfavour, and was denounced by the official party organ, *Culture and Life*, as anaemic and one-sided.

Meanwhile Zhdanov had been giving unmistakable warnings to the intellectuals. He denounced " academic " and " objective " research as an occupation unworthy of Marxist scholars, who must be militant, partisan and intolerant. " ' Partisanship in the proletarian world view,' it was later explained in Moscow, ' did not exclude objectivity in the study of facts, but on the contrary presupposed it, since the class interests of the proletariat do not contradict but coincide with the objective course of historical development.' "

History books were revised to meet the new situation. For instance, " the 1945 edition of a textbook on Russian history by A. Pankratova included Stalin's appraisal of the Allied landing in Normandy as a ' brilliant success '—' the history of war knows no other enterprise like it for breadth of purpose, grandiose skill and masterful execution.' The 1946 edition limited its account to a bare statement that ' on June 6th, 1944, Allied forces accomplished a landing in Northern France.' "

But the historians were thoroughly frightened, and " without exception . . . refused to climb out on a limb by writing text-books, surveys, or monographs on the history of the Soviet regime after the death of Lenin."

A popular collective student textbook, " History of the U.S.S.R.," originally written in 1939, was revised in 1947 to bring it into line with party requirements, but the revision was sharply attacked by *Bolshevik*, an organ of the Central Committee of the Party, and a further revision was ordered.

In 1948 the prominent historian Rubinstein indulged in a confession of his own shortcomings. " He openly deplored his having become a victim of a ' formal,' ' objective,' and ' academic ' approach instead of having adopted the only admissible ' militant party outlook ' in dealing with scientific problems [*science* in the U.S.S.R. is used in the customary continental sense to cover all branches of learning, and not merely natural science]. Hence his main fault was that he presented the historical theories of Lenin and Stalin as ' the outcome of previously existing progressive historical thought instead of interpreting them as the foundation of an entirely new revolutionary science of history.' " We shall see later that this same insistence on the absolute novelty of official Soviet thought was also made in philosophy.

In September 1948, an official writer in *Historical Questions* said that the state of affairs on the " historical front " was far from satisfactory. " Soviet historians have still not acquired the real militant party spirit advocated by Stalin . . . They are unwilling to quarrel . . . and they preserve the rotten tradition of blind devotion to learned ' authorities ' inherited from pre-revolutionary days."

The present position is stated to be that " the ' ideal ' historian must be trained to derive ' theoretical generalizations ' in line with party doctrines and must be free from ' excessive love for facts.' For, as has been recently stated in Moscow,[1] ' where theory fails to play

---

[1] In a publication of the Academy of Sciences, *Izvestia Akademii Nauk SSSR*, Otdel. ekon i prava, 1948, No. 3, p. III.

a leading role in research, vices are bound to appear—such as rotten liberalism, ideological weakening and lack of criticism and self-criticism.' "

In philosophy, restriction appears to operate by reference to a tradition of authority and orthodoxy. In 1947 there was a discussion on philosophy centering round the *History of Western European Philosophy*, by G. F. Alexandrov, one of the outstanding philosophers in the U.S.S.R., and at the time himself a member of the Central Committee. A summary of the discussion was later published in the French review *Europe*. To read this is rather like being transported back to one of the Councils of early Christianity, except that the authorities with whom one must conform are not the Fathers of the Church, but the Fathers of the Revolution—Marx, Engels, Lenin and Stalin.

The Central Committee of the Communist Party took a prominent part in the discussion, in the person of Andrei Alexandrovich Zhdanov. Zhdanov, (who has since died) was a very powerful political figure, famous as the defender of Leningrad, who in the last years of his life became very much concerned with the problems of subordinating thought and expression to what I may perhaps call ideological expediency, and was the Central Committee's spokesman on cultural matters, and their agent in all the cultural reforms and purges which it undertook since the end of the war.

The gist of his attack was that Alexandrov had stated that various elements in Marxist philosophy could be traced back to the work of pre-Marxist philosophers ; and that he had been " objective," instead of being " partisan " and waging a determined offensive against hostile ideology. His history of philosophy should not have been neutral, but should have recorded the history of the struggle of materialism with idealism.

As Werth (1949) writes, " He (Zhdanov) decreed, in effect, that henceforth pre-Marxist philosophy must be treated on an entirely different plane from Marxist philosophy, for Marxist philosophy alone was scientific, while all pre-Marxist philosophy was speculative. Such was the gist of the argument. This crude over-simplification deeply embarrassed foreign Marxists ; but Zhdanov did not care."

The view that Soviet philosophy must become nationalistic and devote itself exclusively to strengthening the position of Communisn is borne out by the recantation of Professor Kedrov, reported in the London *Times* of March 23, 1949. Professor Kedrov's suggestion of international solidarity among scientists and philosophers had been denounced as " monstrous " in an article in the Soviet Literary Gazette on March 9, and the Scientific Council of the State Institute of Philosophy had recently recommended his removal from its membership.

In a letter in the official periodical *Culture and Life* of March 22, Professor Kedrov admitted having adopted mistaken positions in philosophy. He declared that " bourgeois cosmopolitanism " was " an ideological weapon of American imperialism," and that " the slightest advocacy of cosmopolitic viewpoints is direct treason to the cause of Communism."

Henceforth the function of philosophy in the U.S.S.R. is not to explore the basis of human thought and action in general, but to clarify and develop a particular philosophy, that of neo-Marxism (as we may call Marxism as brought up-to-date since 1917), which provides the theoretical basis for political activity.

In the field of law, Andrei Vishinsky's " The Law of the Soviet State " (reviewed in the New Republic, February 7, 1949) illustrates how Soviet law is focussed on a political task. Further, as the reviewer says, it is not only a compendium but a revolutionary handbook and a " hagiography " glorifying Marx, Engels, Lenin and Stalin and attacking their opponents such as Trotsky and Bukharin.

It is worth recalling that since 1934, special boards have been in existence with jurisdiction over persons " recognized as socially dangerous," though not necessarily accused of any criminal act (Hazard, in [8], p. 17).

In the arts, on the other hand, the positive criterion to which they must conform is " socialist realism," as opposed to the negative criterion of " formalism." These criteria are interpreted rather differently in different arts—in music, for example, a good deal of subtlety has to be employed to give a sense to the term *realism* ; but rather crudely it may be said that " socialist realism " is intended as the justification of the belief that the arts should be easily intelligible to every citizen, and should have as their only, or at least their prime, function the social one of providing emotional outlet, focus and drive for the activities of society in war and peace, as against that of new exploration or of expression for the individual artist, or of private enjoyment by the individual citizen. Socialist realism must also be patriotic, so that cosmopolitanism and " servility to the west " are to be condemned. [1]

[1] In Hungary, Professor Lukacs, perhaps the most distinguished Communist philosopher of the day, has recently been attacked for the " deviationism " exhibited in his new book on art and democracy. (Times, July 3, 1949). He is accused especially of anti-Soviet unpatriotic

In the field of literature, Zhdanov in 1946 had made a violent speech denouncing the brilliant satirist and humorist Zoschenko ' for his " cheap hee-hawing " at Soviet reality,' and another accusing the poetess 'Anna Akhmatova—" half nun, half harlot," as he called her, for living nostalgically and egocentrically in the past ' (Werth, 1949). Akhmatova was officially condemned because her poems could, in the opinion of the authorities, " only sow gloom, low spirits, pessimism, the desire to escape from the vital problems of social life " (Langdon-Davies, 1949). Zoschenko, whose humour must have provided a safety-valve for millions of Russians, was " castigated as a writer who helped to disintegrate and corrupt literature " (Slonim, in [8], p. 105), and both he and Akhmatova were expelled from the Union of Soviet Writers. Nothing by either of them has been published for nearly two years.

I myself heard Fadeyev, at the Wroclaw Conference of Intellectuals, attack the writings of a number of Western men of letters, including T. S. Eliot (who shortly afterwards was awarded the Nobel prize for literature), ending up by saying that " if hyenas could use fountain pens and jackals could use typewriters, this is how they would write."

Almost the only objective fact in Fadeyev's lengthy speech was his statement that two million copies of his book " The Young Guard," had been published. Yet Werth, who knows a good deal about Russian literature, describes his book as " a dreary hackwork in which the heroic passions and deeds of the underground resistance organization in the mining town of Kras-

cosmopolitanism, and is also taken to task for asserting the autonomy of art by stating that " neither decrees nor directions can deflect art into a new line of development. This only artists themselves can do, not, of course, independently of changes in life and society."

nodar are described with the literary finesse of Ethel M. Dell."

Fadeyev himself, though promoted in 1946 to the highest position in the Union of Soviet Writers, did not escape criticism. In 1947 he was accused of " deviation " and of not having sufficiently stressed in *The Young Guard*, the role of the party in the youth movement. As a prominent critic wrote, " the criticisms of *The Young Guard* clearly reveal that the vast historical content of our era cannot be fully expressed in a work of art unless the latter describes the great role played by the party in the life of the people."

However, Fadeyev has since been fully restored to favour.

Werth points out that the whole Soviet propaganda machine and all the resources of the State-controlled publishing houses are given the task of boosting books which are officially favoured, which is one very effective way of imposing ideology on literature.

Werth also points out that that really great writer Sholokhov must in some way have fallen from favour, as he has published nothing for over ten years.

Slonim (in [8], pp. 101-113) writes on *Soviet Prose after the War*. The place of literature in society " is very important, for its emotional and intellectual role is recognized by all party theoreticians. If writers, as Stalin put it, are ' engineers of human souls,' the way they pursue their delicate job is, of necessity, of great concern to the rulers of the country. Literature helped to win the war. Now it is harnessed to help the party in the task of consolidating its ideological stability " . . . " The new literary policy was officially formulated on August 14th, 1948, in a resolution of the Central Committee of the All-Union Communist Party. This

resolution has since been commented upon and en-
larged upon in explanatory speeches by the late Andrei
Zhdanov, member of the Politburo, in articles and
speeches by Alexander Fadeyev, secretary of the Union
of Soviet Writers, and in hundreds of articles in the
daily press and periodicals, which repeat the same
arguments in monotonously identical terms. All these
statements emphasize the need to strengthen the ideological awareness of Soviet literature. Zhdanov made
this very plain : ' Soviet literature neither has nor can
have any other interests except those of the people and
of the State. Its aim is to help the State to educate the
youth . . . to make the new generation cheerful, inspired by faith in their task, unafraid of obstacles and
ready to overcome them all.'

"Almost every Communist critic quoted Lenin's
words : ' Literature must become party literature.
Down with non-party literati, down with literary super-
men ! Literary work must become a part of all proletarian endeavour ! ' The purpose of literature should
be ' to portray the Soviet man and his moral qualities
in all their force and completeness.' In other words,
literature must describe the new hero, reared by the
Soviet regime, and glorify those virtues that the state
deems necessary for the triumph of its ideology.

"In performing this task, Soviet literature must
' maintain its integrity and protect itself against the
poisonous miasmas of western bourgeois art,' Zhdanov
as well as the Central Committee warned the writers
against the lures and wiles of decadent Europe and
America. Imitation of western writers was one of the
worst crimes a Soviet writer could commit. ' Is it
becoming to our advanced Soviet literature,' asked .
Zhdanov, ' the most revolutionary literature of the

world, to kowtow to the narrow, petty bourgeois literature of the west ? ' . . .

" Two main points are continually stressed by party authorities : literature must be optimistic, and it must prove the superiority of the Soviet way of life over that of the west. The latter requirement involves the presentation of the non-Soviet world as morally decadent and ideologically confused."

One immediate effect of the resolution was the suspension of one important literary magazine, *Leningrad*, and the radical reform of a second, *The Star*. Another was the launching of a campaign, which culminated in 1948, " against ' bourgeois liberalism ' in literary scholarship . . . The main object of this campaign was to prove that Russia's literary tradition and her cultural heritage were free from western influence "— yet another example of the isolationism and cultural autarky dictated by " Soviet patriotism." The over-all result was the canalizing of Soviet literature along the ideological channels laid down by the communist party, a process which is still in operation.

Englishmen were able to see for themselves to what a low level Soviet graphic art had been reduced by the doctrines of Socialist realism, when a selection of it was exhibited at the Royal Academy a few years ago.

For the details of the disciplining of music, I must refer my readers to the fully documented and informed discussion in Werth's book. Here I can only mention a few points of particular interest.

The method of a conference was used here, as in genetics. However, the conference (which took place in January, 1948) was a private one, of composers and musicians, apparently convened by the Central Committee of the Communist Party, and held in its offices.

The result of the Conference was a Decree of the Central Committee, issued in February, 1948, which laid down a party line for music.

Again, as in genetics, a decisive role was played by one man—in this case Zhdanov, under whose chairmanship the Conference took place. Although he appears to have had no professional competence in the subject, rumours were spread that he was an accomplished musician, and a graduate of the Leningrad Conservatory.

The two main criteria applied by him to music were that it should be intelligible to " the People," and should be in the classical tradition, especially the classical Russian tradition. By intelligibility, Zhdanov meant immediate intelligibility. He paid no attention to the well-known fact that, as Werth says, " scarcely any musical work ' registers ' right away with the listener," and that accordingly a familiarizing process is necessary. Furthermore, he dismissed or neglected the problem of raising the level of popular appreciation. The Decree itself states that " the divorce between some Soviet composers and the people is so serious that these composers have been indulging in the rotten " theory " that the People are not sufficiently grown up to appreciate their music."

Just as purely scientific standards were rejected in the genetics controversy, so here purely musical standards were rejected. The only standard allowed was that of the taste of the masses. Although " formalism " is used as a criterion of condemnation, one can find no meaning attached to it except that of being divorced from Soviet reality, i.e. of not appealing immediately to the People. The Decree itself states that the Central Committee resolves " to condemn the formalist tendency in Soviet music as anti-People and as leading to the liquidation of music."

The criterion of conformity to the classical tradition is entangled with patriotism and with the growth of anti-foreign ideology. During the discussion, the critic and musical historian Keldysh went so far as to say " our art must express the Communist ideology, and must not borrow anything even from what is best in foreign countries."[1]

But this return to the past has been very noticeable for some time, especially in ballet and opera. At the Academy celebrations in Moscow in 1945, during an entr'acte of Chaikovsky's Swan Lake, I enthused over the performance to a French acquaintance, a great connoisseur. " Yes, yes," he said " but I am getting a little tired of fossil ballet." And it was true. The visitors were offered nothing but 19th century ballet and 19th century opera and 19th century drama. It was all beautifully presented, but the presentation itself was entirely traditional—so traditional that only full length three-act ballets were ever staged. The one-act ballet, which has given the world so much of beauty and enjoyment, was not permitted. According to a few inquiries that I made, there were no 20th century ballets in the repertoire of the Bolskoi Theatre at that time, although a new one by Prokofiev was shortly due for performance.

It is strange to think that Glinka and Chaikovsky are now the models for Soviet musicians, and that the music of revolutionary Communism has been ordered

[1] The criteria for determining whether a musician is in the classical Russian tradition appear to be simple : he must be Russian, and he must be pre-revolutionary in date. Scriabin thus becomes a classic, although in point of fact he was guilty of formalism, atonalism, egocentricity, unintelligibility and other " anti-People " tendencies.

to turn back to that of 19th century Tsarism. In default of real criteria for Socialist realism in music, the growth of nationalist feeling combined with the demand for intelligibility has led to this paradoxical result.

Other unpleasant features of the music discussion, which it shared with the genetics controversy, were the violent abuse hurled at the unfortunate scapegoats, like Shostakovich, Prokofiev, and Khachaturian,[1] the general scrambling to be on the band-wagon, and the spite and malice exhibited by many of the second-rate musicians, during the trouble and after it, when some of them came into positions of authority in the U.S.S.R.

In natural science, it is too much to suggest that everything shall be readily intelligible to everybody. On the other hand, there is apparently in many fields, and perhaps notably in agriculture, a tendency to stress the practical aspects of science in providing control over nature, as against the ' pure ' aspect, as providing knowledge and understanding of nature. It is therefore sought to associate the practical workers in applied science as closely as possible with research ; and to achieve this it is desirable that scientific theories should be of as simple a nature as possible. Elaborate and unfamiliar theoretical constructions (such as that of neo-Mendelism) cannot be expected to appeal to the practical man who is anxious for results and likes to feel he understands the great adventure in which he

[1] The decree itself after mentioning them by name accuses them of " formalist perversions and anti-democratic tendencies which are alien to the Soviet people and their artistic tastes," labels them as " the anti-People School," and ascribes to them " a striving after chaotic and neuropathic discord and accumulation of sounds." The press and some of the speakers in the discussion were even more violent : thus Professor Goldenweiser was " horrified to feel that they [various new symphonies and sonatas] are akin to the decadent ideology of the West —or even of Fascism."

is participating. They can therefore be conveniently discouraged by being branded as formalist (as well as being stigmatized as politically undesirable, if that too is required).

The attack on the theory of probability is another example of the appeal to naïve practicability. Soviet science does not want mere probability in its theories, because it wants certainty of results : this is in no sense an unfair travesty of the position taken by Lysenko himself—it would presumably be over-complicated and difficult to explain that only by means of the theory of probability is it possible to evaluate whatever degree of certainty a scientific result may have. Waddington (1948–49) refers to Lysenko's "puerile belief that it is illegitimate to apply mathematics to living things." [1]

In the general field of statistics, we find the familiar phenomenon of the exaltation of a distinctively Soviet branch of science. Thus Pisarev in the authoritative publication " Questions of Economics " (No. 7, 1948) writes " The Soviet land is the cradle of a new science of statistics—the statistics of the Socialist society. Created by Lenin and Stalin, Soviet statistics mark a

[1] Thanks to the kindness of Prof. W. Feller of Cornell University, who is an authority on probability theory, I am able to correct the above paragraph and the reference to the subject in Chap. III. It appears that there has been no attack on the pure mathematical theory of probability, in which Russia still maintains a leading position. The attack is directed against the application of probability theory, in the form of mathematical *statistics*, to various branches of science, especially biology, and to practical affairs. Professor Feller writes, " there is practically no statistics in Russia and it is a surprising feature that a country which is so strong in probability theory has made practically no contribution to mathematical statistics. Obviously the political atmosphere is very unfavorable to that type of application."

For a country which maintains that the unity of theory and practice is indispensable for rapid scientific advance, this is very strange. Perhaps when the authorities realize the practical implications of pure *probability theory*, it too will come under fire, as happened in the '30's with pure genetic theory.

radical break in the tradition of scientific methodology, in the organization, practice, content, aims, and tasks of statistics. In the land of the Soviet, statistics have become a weapon for building Socialism and Communism . . . Lenin and Stalin solved the basic nodal problems of the science of statistics . . . . It is a matter of honour for Soviet statisticians to conduct a militant Party criticism and to unmask bourgeois statistics, the worthlessness of its 'scientific' bases, its decay, its impotence, and its apologist role, and also to uproot all signs of obsequiousness to bourgeois science."

After this book was already in proof, reports have appeared showing that astronomy has also been attacked (see *New York Times*, July 17th, 1949, E. 11). The attack is directed primarily against relativity theory in general, and also against the idea of a finite but expanding universe, which many western astronomers regard as a consequence of relativity theory. This, it appears, has been officially rejected by the Soviet Academy of Sciences. During the debate, one of the speakers described relativity as a "cancerous tumor that gnaws through modern astronomical theory and is the main ideological enemy of materialist astronomy."

This is a continuation of a general attack on relativity, which so far back as 1938 was described as "counter-revolutionary" by the Astronomical Section of the Academy of Sciences. The reason for this attitude appears to be simple, namely, that theory of relativity does not fit in with the materialism of official Marxism, which was based on the general materialist attitude of much of 19th century science. Like other developments of physics, it can easily be represented as "metaphysical," or even "mystical."

In the particular case of genetics, it would seem that Lysenko's theories have a greater appeal to the practical man because, of their *simpliste* nature, in equating the highly complex processes of heredity to the apparently simpler and, at any rate, more familiar ones of digestion and assimilation, and in their naïve view that environment acts directly upon heredity to produce adaptation, instead of indirectly *via* the mechanism of selection ; and further, in using Michurin's homely ideas, such as the ' shaking ' or ' shattering ' of the ' heredity ', instead of trying to analyse what really happens in the complex biological entities and processes that are actually involved.

Many branches of Russian science have not been treated in the same fashion as genetics. There appears to be no specifically Marxian ideology, still less any party line, prescribed for chemistry or biochemistry, for mathematics (apart from probability theory), for geology, paleontology, ecology, taxonomy, plant physiology, etc. This is presumably because their pursuit has not yet raised any issues of ideological importance.

Whatever the reasons, the " socialization " of biological science in the U.S.S.R. has proceeded along the lines I have indicated : appeal to immediate utility to the partial or total exclusion of the appeal to the discovery of new facts and new truth ; appeal to national patriotism and class sentiment, so that science is regarded primarily as an instrument of the class struggle and its international extensions; the subordination of scientific to philosophical theory, and of scientific activity to an over-riding socio-political point of view ; and finally, the appeal to authority, in the shape of a party line, in regard to scientific theory, scientific research and scientific education. In passing, it must be noted that a great deal of what may be called the philosophical labelling of tendencies in science has been exceedingly arbitrary, and often, in my opinion, actually erroneous. Thus, as already mentioned, it is a perversion of terms to call neo-Mendelism *idealist* and *anti-materialist* when its chief merit has been the discovery of the material basis of inheritance. As regards the name-calling of individual geneticists, I knew Morgan intimately, and know that it is absurd to impute any philosophical or political motives to him; and Muller, who is now stigmatized as ' bourgeois ' or ' reactionary,' was actually in difficulties in the United States for some years of his most fruitful period because of his left-wing and pro-Russian attitude. In any case, a fact is a fact, whether discovered by a communist or a fascist, whether in the U.S.A. or in the U.S.S.R.

So far I have endeavoured to describe the genetics controversy, to state the issues which it involves, and to give some brief account of the situation in other fields of thought and creative expression in the U.S.S.R. But I am sure that there is a question mark in my readers' minds. *Why* ? Why have the Soviet authorities acted thus ? Why do they favour a Lamarckian theory and exhibit such hostility to Mendelian genetics ? Why this constant preoccupation with ideology ? Why do they lay down an official line for intellectual and artistic matters ? Why did the Academy of Sciences consent to be a party to the subordination of scientific truth to other considerations ?

I do not suppose that anyone outside the U.S.S.R. could be sure of the answers to such questions, and I certainly am not. But it is possible, I think, to render

173

the situation a little more intelligible.

First of all, the insistence on ideology, which has as its consequence the dragging in of philosophical criteria, such as formalism and materialism, into any and every subject, whether scientific, political, or aesthetic. We must remember that the Russian revolution and the Soviet State itself has a theoretical basis, in the shape of Marxist Communism, with its philosophy of dialectical materialism. Many people, indeed, have pointed out that Communism today is in practice a religion or a substitute for a religion, providing a driving force for the developing Socialist society. Like most other movements of a religious or pseudo-religious nature, or with a social function similar to that of a religion, it has its " theology " in the shape of an intellectual and dogmatic framework.

Marxism as an intellectual construction has naturally been developed and extended with the passage of time, and its interpretation has been adjusted to meet particular crises. Lenin did a great deal in this direction, so that at one period we heard a great deal of Marxist-Leninist principles. Stalin has also continued the process of developing Communist theory, and under his influence many changes in practice and in interpretation have been introduced. But it has always retained its importance as official dogma, for a set of dogmatic beliefs and principles seems to be indispensable to any totalitarian society.

The chief general dogma of Communism is the belief in dialectical materialism and the materialist interpretation of history. Materialism is an official philosophy. This has had as one effect the discouragement of psychological research, and the substitution of such work as that of Bechterew and Pavlov, with its attempted materialistic interpretation of mind.[1]

The most important special dogma of Communism is the belief in the class struggle as determining political history. The present phase of the class struggle is between capitalism and (communist) socialism. According to Marxist dogma, this struggle is an irreconcilable one, and can only be terminated by the revolutionary overthrow of capitalism by communism. It is also an article of belief that communism must and will eventually win, but that its victory demands conscious struggle and effort on the part of its adherents.

Certain consequences flow directly from these dogmas. In the first place, any philosophical doctrine or scientific theory must somehow be able to justify itself as being *materialist* if it is to be acceptable. And conversely, since the official opposite of materialism is idealism, any doctrine or theory to which there attaches a suspicion of *idealism* will be under grave handicap.

The term *materialism* thus comes to have two different meanings, or perhaps I should say, two different semantic functions. At one moment it is used as a description : it describes the attempt to interpret reality wholly in terms of matter. At another it is used as a certificate of value : it becomes a label, and a label which carries with it implications of praise and commendation, to denote conformity with official dogma. The same of course applies to idealism, but the other way round.

Since it is officially laid down that dialectical materialism alone among philosophies is truly scientific, the term *scientific* also comes to be used as a label and a term of approval, irrespective of whether the activity

[1] Hudson and Richens (1946, p. 4 *ff*) discuss some of the consequences of dialectical materialism for Soviet biology.

to which the label is attached is really being conducted in a scientific way. On the other side of the fence, since metaphysics and mysticism are considered to be incompatible with materialism, the terms *metaphysical* and *mystic* also acquire the function of labels—labels of disapproval.

This being the case, it is small wonder that discussion in the U.S.S.R., whether of scientific or political, of artistic or intellectual subjects, should involve the frequent employment of ideological labels. It makes the discussion more difficult for the westerner to understand, but is itself very understandable, as a direct consequence of the existence of an official philosophy or dogma. Furthermore, human nature being what it is, it is inevitable that such labels shall be often attached with the deliberate purpose of strengthening one's own case or weakening that of an opponent, but with little relevance to the facts of the case. We can thus understand *why* Lysenko and his followers call Mendelism " idealist," although it is actually so materialist that it has shown us how (to quote Sewall Wright), " heredity may be sucked out of an egg with a micropipette " ; or " mystical " or " anti-scientific," although their own doctrine of the inheritance of acquired characters is little more than a survival of sympathetic magic, and their theory of heredity wholly pre-scientific in its formulation. They do so because they have to do so in order to appear orthodox, and because it pays to do so in order to emerge victorious in the dispute.

The particular dogma concerning the inevitability of the conflict between capitalism and communism has other consequences. According to this dogma, according to this doctrine, the developing socialist society of the U.S.S.R. in particular, and of communist countries in general, finds itself involved in a desperate and inevitable struggle with capitalist society in the other major countries of the world. Not only is that struggle inevitable, but it admits of no compromise : according to the official philosophy of Soviet communism, it must continue until the victory of communism is assured.

Science accordingly comes to be regarded as an organ of the developing socialist society and therefore as one of its weapons in its struggle against the rest of the world. Furthermore, the socio-political struggle is transferred into science, which is then seen as divided into two camps, as inevitably and as irreconcilably opposed as, in the view of orthodox Soviet political philosophy, are communism and capitalism, the communist and the bourgeois or capitalist type of society.

It has puzzled many observers to note that, in the genetics controversy, the official Soviet scientists have abandoned one element in orthodox Marxism, namely the principle that advance is effected through the reconciliation of opposites, by the reconciliation of thesis and antithesis in a higher synthesis. However, the explanation is, I think, the simple one I have just advanced, namely, that the scientific controversy has been subordinated to and indeed made a part of the class struggle, and so has come to partake of the irreconcilability which the Marxists have always pronounced to be a feature of the more general socio-political conflict.[1]

---

[1] The same is true for culture. At the Wroclaw Congress of Intellectuals last summer, several Soviet speakers, including Ilya Ehrenberg, were strong in denunciation of Western or bourgeois culture and ideology, and emphatic in asserting that there could be no reconciliation between them and Soviet culture and ideology—or rather no compromise, since this avoids the use of the ideologically awkward term *reconciliation.*

One further consequence of this state of affairs is the injection of patriotism and xenophobia into science, as we have already cited. For some little time past, rebukes have been administered to Soviet scientific workers for servility to foreign or bourgeois scientific theories, and the principle of secrecy in science has been extended further in the U.S.S.R. than elsewhere, since Soviet scientists in general, and not only those engaged on war research, have been warned not to speak freely to foreign scientists about scientific discoveries in the U.S.S.R.

This gives rise to a new set of labels, *Bourgeois* and *capitalist* become terms of ideological abuse ; and to be able to call a theory or a fact *foreign* becomes a ground for calling it *unpatriotic*.

In this field, cause and effect are entangled. The Russians deliberately glorify a plant-breeder like Michurin because they want a basis of patriotism for Soviet genetics ; and once Michurin is officially glorified, his utterances acquire a special authority which can be used to confute opponents of the official doctrine.

Another symptom of this patriotic isolationism is the recent cessation by Soviet scientific journals of the traditional practice of publishing abstracts in some other language than Russian (usually English or French) of the contributions which they publish. I cannot state whether this is universal, but it is certainly widespread, and must accentuate the scientific and cultural isolation of the U.S.S.R.

Once any over-riding system of ideological criteria is set up for science, it becomes all too easy for men of science who enjoy political power or are in a position of authority to use it for the discomforture of their scientific opponents ; and, in fact, in reading the summary of the discussion on Soviet biology, one cannot escape the conclusion that Lysenko and his followers have thus taken advantage of the situation. Because a system of authority and orthodoxy exists in the U.S.S.R., and because within such a system certain philosophic labels connote blame and condemnation, those labels, it would seem, have often been attached with the deliberate purpose of administering a thorough beating to one party to a scientific dispute.

Totalitarianism involves dogmatic beliefs, so that political totalitarianism inevitably tends towards a totalitarianism of thought. Not only the course and result of the genetics controversy, but also the methods employed in it, can only be understood if we remember that it took place in a totalitarian country.

Russian science in general stands at a high level. How can the Academy have given its blessing to Michurinism, whose facts are notoriously and obviously dubious and whose crude interpretative principles bear no resemblance to a scientific theory in the accepted sense ; and how can it have pronounced the scientific condemnation of Mendelian genetics, seeing that in its fifty years of existence that subject has steadily developed until in all other countries it is accepted as one of the most vigorous and successful branches of science ?

The totalitarianism of the U.S.S.R. appears to provide the only answer to this question. Once an official party line had been laid down for biology, the Academy had to toe it, like everybody else.

It is of interest in this connection as already mentioned (p. 33), that up to 1945–46 the Academy had been seriously considering resolving the genetics controversy by setting up a special Institute to deal with

Mendelian genetics, under Dubinin, so that both parties in the dispute could have continued working on an equal footing. There had been no discovery or other scientific happening since then which could have influenced their decision ; the only relevant event was that Michurinism had been officially approved and Mendelism officially disapproved.

But all this leaves unanswered the question why official approval was given to Michurinism. As I suggested at the end of Chapter 3, Lysenko seems to have owed his power to political backing. But why should the politicians have wanted to back Lysenko ? Why did they like Lamarckism and dislike Mendelism ?

How could the political authorities have given official sanction to and exclusive encouragement to Michurinism, when impartial scientific advice, if given without any political pressure, would have told them that its methods and ideas, when not definitely false, are inadequate and unscientific, in that they do not meet normal scientific criteria ? Do they not know that bad science cannot produce good practical results ?

I think that there are two main reasons, one practical, the other ideological. The practical reason is that the U.S.S.R. is still economically and technologically a backward country, with much leeway still to make up and many opportunities still unexploited. This is very much so in agriculture, and in agriculture the need for rapid improvement is particularly pressing. The entire Soviet standard of life depends upon an increase in agricultural yield.

Lysenko's theory held out the promise of a much more rapid increase of yield than does Mendelism ; and his practice since 1935 seemed evidence of successful achievement.

As a matter of fact, Lysenko's success was in large measure due to the fact of Soviet agricultural backwardness. In a country with antiquated methods, any modernization of technique will have a salutary effect. Much of his success is due to the introduction of new agronomical methods, which have nothing to do with heredity ; but his success in this field has added to his general prestige in all agricultural matters.

Again, in a country where the strains of crop-plants and livestock are relatively unimproved and far from genetically pure, as appears to be the case in the U.S.S.R., almost any energetic attempt at improvement will have considerable practical results in the first few years. And Lysenko is undoubtedly energetic. What matter that his results are in all probability due to the strictly neo-Darwinian process of mass selection, sometimes following on the strictly neo-Mendelian process of increased variability after crossing—the results are successful.

It is worth pointing out, however, that mass selection cannot go on producing rapid results.[1] It soon reaches a point of diminishing returns ; and after this is reached, it is necessary to employ special methods based on Mendelian theory to secure any considerable improvement.

The outstanding example of this is the success of hybrid maize (corn) in the U.S.A. This was developed entirely on a basis of neo-Mendelian theory by G. H. Shull, D.F. Jones, East and other American geneticists. It involves strict inbreeding (which purges the stock of deleterious recessives), and then crossing the inbred lines in particular ways to provide the maximum of what is known as hybrid vigour (which depends on a

[1] See Sewall Wright, in ([6]) ; p. 142.

complex interaction of complementary genes in the different inbred lines). The inbred lines, lacking hybrid vigour, look (and are) miserable ; but the new hybrids are immensely superior to the original strain. Nearly 100,000 inbred lines were prepared and tested in the course of the work.

This procedure is estimated to have increased the corn crop [in the U.S.A.] by half a billion bushels a year. Some 90 per cent. of the corn in the Corn Belt is now hybrid corn ([6], p. 142). Each year something like 200,000 tons or more of hybrid seed is used for planting. (Haskell—1949.)

" During the war, the use of hybrid corn seed permitted our farmers to grow in two years what normally would require three years with the old type varieties. Hybrid corn is worth about $1,000,000,000 a year to the farmers " of the U.S.A. (*ibid* p. 146).

It is a great pity for the U.S.S.R. that they were in such a hurry and that they would not trust neo-Mendelian theory. On seeing the poor quality of the lines produced by intensive inbreeding, the Michurinites decided against " time-consuming inbreeding procedures " and in favour of direct selection from the original strains. This undoubtedly will have had a rapid effect over a short period, but the improvement will have been much less than what they could have obtained by following in the footsteps of the neo-Mendelians in America.

It must also be remembered that Lysenko is a man of great energy, and that he enjoys the confidence of the peasants and agricultural workers in general ; and that this has certainly contributed to the success of the methods he advocates.

Communism has practical achievement as part of its

ideology. It is part of the job of man, at least of Communist man, to change nature for his own ends. This has had two effects on the genetics controversy. In the first place, it has led to undue weight being attached to the practical function of science in controlling phenomena, as against its intellectual function in understanding them. And in the second place it has led Lysenko and his followers to an unscrupulous misrepresentation of Mendelian genetics as " useless." This has been done partly by referring to the impracticality of researches which were not undertaken for immediate practical ends, but to gain further knowledge of the basic principles of genetics ; partly by neglecting the practical achievements of Mendelian genetics in other countries (such as the hybrid corn I have just mentioned, or the increased yield due to the production, on strict Mendelian principles, of rust-resistant wheats) ; partly by exaggerating the failures of the Russian Mendelians to produce quick practical results.

I now come to the ideological reason for the political backing given to Lysenko. I had perhaps better say reasons, for I think there are two. One is the dislike of Mendelism because Mendelian heredity, with its self-copying genes and its random undirected mutations, seems to offer too much resistance to man's desire to change nature, and to elude the control he would like to impose. Lamarckism, on the other hand, holds out a promise of speedy control. The methods that it advocates are simple and easy to understand, while Mendelism insists on elaborate and abstruse procedures which are beyond the comprehension of the uninstructed farmer or the uninstructed politician.

This is relevant not only in agriculture, but also in human affairs, for it would be politically very convenient and agreeable if a few generations of life under improved Communist conditions would level up the genetic quality of the population of the U.S.S.R.

Muller has told me of two incidents, during his stay in Russia, which bear this out. In private conversation, a political figure admitted to him that the powers that be did not really believe in the genetic equality of all the different races that inhabit the U.S.S.R., but comforted himself by saying that even the most striking genetic inferiorities would be rapidly got rid of by the improved conditions which successful communism would bring about.

While in the U.S.S.R., Muller wrote *Out of the Night* (one of the most interesting books on eugenics I know). The book starts from the premise that only in a society in which class and heredity privileges had been abolished could one detect which differences between human beings are due to differences in their genetic make-up, and which to environment ; and it goes on to point out how, once equality of environment had been provided, methods based on modern (neo-Mendelian) genetics could be applied, to produce a quite rapid and all-round increase in the average level of desirable human qualities such as physique, health, and general intelligence.

He arranged for the MS to be transmitted to the highest quarters ; but it was ill received, (partly, it appears, because it postulated human inequality, but also because some of the methods advocated, such as artificial insemination from a few superior fathers, were considered by the very high personage in question as " an insult to Soviet womanhood "). As a result, the unfortunate Russian geneticist who had acted for Muller in the matter fell into disgrace.

This brings in the second ideological reason involved. It is a dislike of Mendelism because it implies human inequality, and because it can be taken to imply human helplessness in the fact of genetic predestination. Mendelism makes it clear that no two human being (save identical twins) are endowed with the same outfit of genes ; and that all characters, of mind as well as body, are in part determined by genes. The human species is a mass of genetic inequality ; and human beings are not merely different from each other, but often differ in respect of a greater or lesser genetic endowment of desirable characters like health or intelligence.

Furthermore, if a man is what his genes make him, what is the use of human aspiration or effort ?

The idea of human inequality must be distasteful to those responsible for directing a professedly egalitarian society. Professor J. R. S. Haldane, in an essay published in 1932, foresaw that there might be a danger to Russian science arising from its intimate association with the State. " It may possibly be that, as a result of that association, science in Russia will undergo somewhat the same fate as overtook Christianity after its association with the State in the time of Constantine. It is possible that it may lead to dogmatism in science and to the suppression of opinions which run counter to official theories . . . The test of the devotion of the U.S.S.R. to science will, I think, come when the accumulation of the results of human genetics, demonstrating what I believe to be the fact of innate human inequality, becomes important."

Professor Haldane was very far-sighted. The first important attack in science was the shutting down of the Medicogenetical Institute in 1936, as mentioned in Chapter 1. The first time that a scientific party line was laid down was in 1948, for genetics and evolution.

Another reason for disliking the idea of genetic inequality is that it has been used in an attempt to justify various reactionary views and bad social practices—Nazi racialism, with its stress on the inevitable superiority of the so-called Aryan (or Nordic, or Germanic) " race " ; unscientific brands of eugenics, which advocate wholesale sterilization of the poorer classes or alleged inferior racial groups ; the colour-bar, Jim Crow laws, and other forms of racial discrimination.

The pro-Lysenko politicians have apparently jumped to the conclusion that acceptance of Mendelism automatically means the acceptance of racialism. In point of fact, it does not do so, any more than acceptance of the biological struggle for existence as a fact means that war is a good thing in human affairs.

Actually, the effect of environment and social conditions is often so large as quite to mask the underlying genetic inequality ; and the genetic variability of the human species is so well distributed that the average genetic difference between different classes or social groups and different nations or ethnic groups is negligible or small in its effects compared with the improvements which can be effected through better living conditions and better education.

Similarly, genetic predetermination is not absolute—environment is needed for the unfolding of man's potentialitites. And in any case (as orthodox Marxism has long pointed out with regard to economic determinism), a result may be inevitable, and yet free will and effort may be necessary agencies for achieving it.

It is, by the way, curious that the anti-Mendelians have not realized that Lamarckism would create even greater theoretical difficulties than Mendelism. If the effects of the environment are imprinted on or assimilated by heredity, then centuries of poverty, ignorance, disease, and oppression should have ingrained a most undesirable heredity upon the vast majority of the human species, and engrained it so firmly that a few generations of improved conditions could not be expected to effect much amelioration. Mendelism, on the other hand, makes it clear that even after long-continued bad conditions, an enormous reserve of good genetic potentiality can still be ready to blossom into actuality as soon as improved conditions provide an opportunity.

It seems clear that there have been many factors at work which have favoured the official enthronement of Michurinism and the official banning of Mendelism—practical ones such as the anxiety for quick results in agriculture, ideological ones such as the dislike of the idea of human inequality, political ones such as the intensification of patriotism and of an anti-foreign nationalism, social ones such as the demand for ready intelligibility of science and art, personal ones such as Stalin's Lamarckian leanings and the existence of Lysenko. It is impossible for an outsider to evaluate their relative importance. All he can do is to point out that they exist, and that the different tendencies must have reinforced each other in a cumulative way.

He can also point out two other factors which were necessary conditions for the result—political totalitarianism and the existence of an official ideology and set of beliefs.

The consequence has been the growth of a new

conception of science, as something conditioned by the society in which it is practised, and subordinated to the needs of that society, a tool for achieving immediate practical results and a weapon in the nation's conflict with other nations. And the final result has been the disruption of science into two separate and hostile parts —Soviet science and bourgeois or capitalist science.

However, none of these circumstances really extenuates the error or crime (in science the two can often be equated) of repudiating scientific method and rejecting the appeal to fact, and, in so doing, of repudiating the unity and the international character of science. All that we can say is that they help us to understand what has happened and why it has happened.

It is, of course, true that the freedom and autonomy of science have been infringed upon in countries other than the U.S.S.R. The total nature of modern war is such that secrecy is imposed on all men of science carrying on research for war purposes, even in peacetime. This, however, affects only a fraction of scientific work. What is in dispute is merely the limit of the ' secret sector ' ; and men of science are still free to devote themselves to work of a non-military nature. Freedom of publication is also limited in certain branches of industrial research ; but here again science as a whole is not involved.

Again, in some countries, such as the Argentine, many university scientists have been dismissed for political reasons. But even in such cases, politics does not presume to dictate the *scientific* admissibility of theories or branches of science.

In recent times the nearest approach in the Western world to ideological control of science was the legislation prohibiting the teaching of evolution in Tennessee and some other States of the U.S.A. But even this was partial in the sense that it affected only a few States, and only the public institutions in those States.

So far as I am aware, in modern times it is only in the U.S.S.R.[1] (and, though to a somewhat lesser extent, in Germany under Hitler) that science has lost its inherent intellectual autonomy, in the sense that the admissibility of its theories, laws and facts is judged not on their scientific merits but in relation to political and philosophical doctrines, and research and scientific thought are subordinated to the directives of a political party.

It will now, I think, be clear that in the U.S.S.R. totalitarianism has now spread from politics and economics to the sphere of intellect and culture. The Soviet State is now provided with a highly organized system of ideas within which thought and creative expression must move. Or, to put the matter slightly differently, the intellectual, scientific, aesthetic and emotional forces of the nation are all harnessed together in a single coherent whole, which we may perhaps for brevity's sake call a cultural system, to work dynamically for one end—the success of the U.S.S.R. in its two-fold aspect of a nation-State competing or co-operating

[1] While this article was being written, the campaign was being extended to other countries within the Russian sphere of influence (see, for example, *Herald Tribune*, Paris, February 22, 1949). In the universities of the Russian Zone in Germany, the professors in biological subjects have been requested to introduce Lysenko's teaching ; in Czechoslovakia an article in the chief organ of the Communist Party extols Lysenko and rebukes " conservative scientists in the West who try to stop what cannot be stopped " ; the Bulgarian Communist Party has demanded the repudiation of the " anti-Marxist biological views of Mendel, Weismann, and Morgan," etc. Western scientists in other fields have also been attacked. Thus the Academy of Sciences has denounced Einstein, Bohr and Heisenberg as " obscurantist " or " bourgeois metaphyscians."

with other nation-States, and as a society embodying the principles of Communism and aiming at their realization in practice.

Soviet policy, though animated by long-term aims which are permanent or at least relatively unchanging, has always been very flexible in its tactics. Accordingly, as we should expect, its cultural system has been closely adapted to the needs of the moment. The chief of these needs, as envisaged by the Soviet authorities, appear to be as follows. A rapid increase of production, both industrial and agricultural ; a firm belief in the Soviet system as superior to all other systems ; the designation of imperialism and capitalism, notably as represented by the U.S.A., as the enemies of Soviet progress ; the participation of the people as a whole in the national effort and in the ideas associated with it ; the strengthening of political discipline and of the position of the Communist Party ; and finally the affirmation of ideological principles.

The resultant is the blend of nationalism and communism which has been called Soviet patriotism ; and the effect has been to accentuate the division of humanity into " two worlds," and to foster the development of isolationism and cultural autarky. The Soviet world is rapidly growing more " thought-tight " : its culture is not only becoming monolithic, but increasingly impervious to cultural influences from outside. Increasing stress is being laid on the ideological inevitability of hostility between the communist and the capitalist world, and the cultural system of the U.S.S.R. is designed to accentuate, not only its distinctiveness but also its natural hostility to western culture.

This is not written by way of judgment or evaluation,

but as an attempt to summarize the facts of the situation, the central fact being that Soviet society is now equipped with a coherent, unified, and dynamic body of ideas, capable of aiding its advance in certain directions.

Far from criticizing or condemning this fact in principle, I ardently wish that the western world had such a valuable auxiliary at its disposal. If our society were wholly or preponderantly animated by a common set of beliefs as to human destiny and the major aims for human progress, we should assuredly be able to achieve that progress much more rapidly. As it is, there is no such agreement, even on such basic questions as the significance of the human individual, the functions of the State, the relations between rights and duties, the proper relation between the spiritual and material factors in life, the roles of science, art and religion, the system of values which we would like to see embodied in society, or the meaning of progress itself. And the result is a sense of frustration and confusion.

I am sure that we could arrive at such a common set of beliefs, if we took advantage of the enormous volume of new knowledge concerning nature and man which has been accumulated during the last two centuries (and in large measure during the last few decades). I am sure that if we did, it would be of the greatest benefit, both in providing the assurance that comes of agreed long-range aims and the energy for dealing with immediate tasks. But I am also sure that it must come willingly, on the basis of agreement and persuasion, not by the mere imposition of authority.

This is where the recent developments in the U.S.S.R. can rightly be criticized. The establishment of a unified system of ideas is not necessarily to be condemned : but the methods by which it has been established may be. What I have called the Soviet cultural system has been imposed upon Soviet society from above, by authority, as a dogma ; force and intimidation and abuse have been employed to bring it about.

It may be said that the methods are an integral part of the system, that the idea that it is right to impose a system of thought forcibly is itself one of the ideas inherent in the system. This is in large measure true. It is perhaps especially relevant for science, where the idea that the appeal of facts can be over-ridden by ideology and authority is an obvious denial of the essential quality and value of science, as a human activity. But in art, or philosophy, or history, the methods used by the Soviet authorities are a denial of freedom—freedom of expression and freedom of thought —and freedom is one of the basic concepts of western society. [1]

I would sum up by saying that the U.S.S.R. has succeeded in socializing thought and expression in all fields, that in so doing it has provided itself with a powerful instrument for furthering its policy, both internal and external ; and that its method has been the method of regimentation through force and authority, which is wrong in principle, and therefore bound to lead eventually to unfortunate results.

There is another feature of Soviet action in this field which also appears to me to be wrong in principle.

[1] I am of course aware that complete laisser-faire individual freedom is undesirable, and that among the major problems of our time are the proper relations between freedom and responsibility, and between freedom and authority (both of them aspects of the broad problem of the relations between the individual and the community) ; but this does not prevent us from regarding freedom as a basic concept of our system.

The aims to which the cultural and ideological system is adjusted are partial and limited. They are the aims of the Soviet State in the mid-twentieth century, and no attention is paid to the general aims of humanity as a whole. In fact, humanity is considered as divided into two inevitably hostile camps, and the form of the cultural system is related to this division.

In any case, as a result of recent events in the U.S.S.R., science as a whole has lost its unity. It is no longer in essential a world activity, that is, one transcending the partial frame-works of nationalism and religion, but has become split into two. The Nazis tried to split it into German, Aryan or Nordic science as opposed to non-Ayran, Jewish or Bolshevik science ; the Russians have now succeeded in splitting it into Soviet, Marxist, Communist or materialist science as against foreign, bourgeois, capitalist or idealist science.

In the west, we believe that science in the proper sense of the word must inevitably be one and international, and that such a separation is unnatural and unreal. To the extent that Soviet science manages to be separate and different from science elsewhere, it will fall short of its possibilities of usefulness and value, not only to humanity at large, but to the U.S.S.R. However, it will take time before these unfortunate consequences are realized in the U.S.S.R. ; and meanwhile the progress of humanity at large towards greater knowledge and greater power is being impeded.

Addendum I While the proofs of this book were being corrected, I received a copy of " Speaking of Peace," the report on the Cultural and Scientific Conference for World Peace, held in March 1949 (New York, National Council of the Arts, Sciences and Professions).

It is too late to discuss here the many points of interest which it contains concerning recent developments in science and culture in the U.S.S.R. I must, however, refer to the remarks of Professor Oparin (p. 43).

In answer to a question, he denied all knowledge as to why Vavilov had been arrested and sent to a Siberian concentration camp, where he died, and said " It seems to me that the gentleman who has just spoken is not well informed." To which one can only retort that Professor Oparin must be singularly ill-informed.

In answer to a further question, he stated that a quotation in *Science* from *Izvestia* was untrue, in which it was reported that a number of professors who were anti-Michurinites had lost their jobs. However, he then proceeded to add that Dubinin " is doing intensive work in reforestation." If so, he *has* lost his job, which was in pure genetics, in favour of a quite different and one would imagine a far less suitable job.

We may presume, until we are assured to the contrary, that the same holds true for the other men who, he stated, were still employed in scientific work. In spite of Prof. Oparin's denials, the fact remains that jobs in Mendelian genetics have been abolished in the U.S.S.R.

Addendum 2. I have just received from Prof. H. Nachtsheim, Director of the Genetics Institute in the Freie Universitat (Free University) of Berlin, some valuable reprints of articles written by him in *Der Tagesspiegel* and other Berlin newspapers. So far as I am aware, this is the first time that the western world has had first-hand information from a good geneticist of what has been happening to genetics in a Russian-dominated area. Prof. Nachtsheim was previously professor in the Humboldt University of Berlin, but as this became more and more closely controlled by the Soviet authorities, felt he must resign and join the newly-founded Free University (*Tagesspiegel*, 1.v.49). In the *Tagesspiegel* for 19.ii.49 he records the following incidents, which occurred while he was still at the Humboldt University.

(1) The new edition of his important book on the domestication of animals, " Vom Wildtier zum Haustier," was to have been printed in the Russian Zone. The (Soviet) " Cultural Advisory Committee on Publishing " refused permission, on the ground that the book did not take sufficient account of the " new genetics " of the U.S.S.R.

(2) One of his assistants had prepared an article on the factors of evolution for publication in a scientific periodical in the Russian Zone. This also was not permitted to be published (a) because it did not take proper account of Lysenko's theories and of Soviet genetics (b) because it mentioned *Timoféeff-Ressovsky*, and his name may not be referred to (cf. the suppression of all reference to Trotsky, which I have elsewhere mentioned).

(Timoféeff-Ressovsky is a Russian who had done outstanding work on mutation in Berlin since 1923. He was removed to Russia in 1945, and his present fate is as obscure as that of Vavilov was for some time. We only know that he was subsequently attacked in Pravda as an " enemy of the Soviet Union." Those who, like myself, were personally acquainted with him, know that he was interested solely in the acquisition of new scientific knowledge !)

(3) A publisher asked Nachtsheim's advice on a school text-book on Darwinism. He stated that it was exceedingly old-fashioned, as well as tendentious, containing nothing whatever about Mendel or the facts of modern genetics, but a great deal about the doctrines of Michurin and Lysenko, as well as much concerning the views of Marx, Engels, Lenin and Stalin, which Nachtsheim regarded as out of place in a school text-book. As Nachtsheim writes, it was " impossible " for modern German readers. As a result, the publisher declined to publish the German translation, and was then accused of " sabotage."

It seems clear that freedom of scientific publication in biology no longer exists in the Russian zone, and that great pressure is being exercised to impose the doctrines of Michurinism in education, while simply not mentioning neo-Mendelism and neo-Darwinism.

Addendum 3. In addition, I now understand that the medical research workers Sergeer and Gause (anti-malarial work) have lost their professional posts, and that the physiologist Lena Stern (artificial resuscitation of electrocuted dogs) is " out of favour."

CHAPTER 6

THE SITUATION OF SCIENCE

Nazi Germany paid for its attacks on scientific autonomy and unity by a deterioration in the quality of its scientific work. The U.S.S.R. will doubtless in due time pay an equally heavy price.[1] But this can provide no satisfaction, except perhaps to the minority whose hostility to the U.S.S.R. over-rides all other considerations. Not only all scientists worthy of the name, but all men who really believe in the possibility of progress for the human species as a whole, and in science as an indispensable agency for securing that progress, all who believe that the search for new truth is one of the highest activities of man, together with all those who believe in intellectual liberty and in freedom of thought and expression, must feel acute regret at the action of the U.S.S.R. through its Academy of Sciences.

But regret is barren. We ask immediately if there is nothing to be done. The answer is yes, there is much to be done, not only by professional natural scientists, but by thinkers and philosophers, by social and political scientists, by politicians and statesmen and administrators, and also by the public at large.

[1] Russian science has already begun to suffer. To mention only genetics and related fields, such notable workers as Vavilov, Levit, Ivanov and Karpechenko have lost their positions in the past, to be followed now by men like Dubinin, Serebrovsky, Gause and Schmalhausen. The ideological atmosphere was such that H. J. Muller relinquished his post after a few years, and excellent Russian geneticists like Dobzhansky and Ephrussi preferred to work in other countries. Among the immediate practical effects of the resolutions of the Academy of Sciences in 1949 is the suppression of the work on cereal and buckwheat polyploids, which in the hands of Zhebrak and of Sacharov was already yielding valuable results.

We need better understanding of the nature and function of scientific method in general ; we also need a better understanding of the relations between science and society, and of the conditions under which the scientific method can operate to the best advantage.

In the first place, we must realize that the action of the U.S.S.R. is only an extreme and exaggerated manifestation of a general situation. The general situation is constituted by the familiar trend towards a greater centralization and a greater organisation of society. This again is regretted by some ; but it would appear to be inevitable in the present stage of the world's history, and many consider it to be a necessary prerequisite not only for the greater efficiency of the social organism but in the long run for the greater happiness and fuller development of individuals. There are, however, good and bad ways, or at least more desirable and less desirable ways, in which this trend can be realized. This applies both to broad social and economic organisation, and also to the way in which science is to be integrated with the rest of the life of society—for clearly science cannot escape the operation of the general trend.

So far as professional men of science are concerned, our question—whether there is nothing to be done—now resolves itself into three more particular questions. What can men of science do to see that the general trend towards the integration of society develops in the best possible way ? What can men of science do to see that the integration of science with other social activities does not infringe on its autonomy and its unity ? And what can men of science do to modify the policy of the U.S.S.R. in subordinating science to philosophical and political orthodoxy ?

Although the first question is perhaps the most important, it is difficult to find an answer to it, and especially a generally agreed answer, and I do not propose to do more than touch upon the matter. I personally would suggest something of this sort. It is of great importance for a society to possess some kind of ideological driving force. National patriotism may suffice in times of war, but not in peace. When religious belief is strong, it may provide the ideological drive ; but this is assuredly not the case in the western world today, where religion is not only fragmented into many churches and sects, but no longer provides a dominant appeal to the majority of people. In the U.S.S.R. and other communist countries, on the other hand, communism does provide such an appeal, and an appeal both theoretical and practical in nature.[1] To provide an equally powerful and equally general appeal, I believe that only some kind of dynamic or evolutionary humanism will suffice, a belief that man has the duty of carrying the general process of evolution to new heights, and that in discharging that duty rightly he will be providing ever-expanding possibilities of fuller living for future generations. If so, then this evolutionary humanism must be partly based primarily on science, and it will be the task of the men of science to provide the material basis for the heightened standards of living, and their share of the theoretical and philosophic background for the new ideology—what for a religion would be its theological frame-work.

The second question is more specific and more immediate. I may perhaps re-phrase it thus : How

[1] Even when the appeal is mainly to the party élite, it is still capable of being used as the theoretical or propaganda background for action or even compulsion, much as theology could be used in the past, in relation, for example, to intolerance or religious persecution.

should men of science act in the face of the increasing concern of the State with science, and the consequent increasing pressure of the State on science ?

Can they accept the existence of an official scientific policy ? Can they accept the possibility that the majority of men of science will be paid by the State and that the major cost of scientific work will be borne on government funds ? Can they accept official direction as to what subjects shall be investigated ?

I think that they can (indeed, that they must)— but with certain clearly formulated provisos. A government is at perfect liberty to embark on a large-scale and comprehensive official scientific policy. It can legitimately decide that that policy shall be predominantly practical—designed to raise the standard of life, to improve health, to increase production, or to promote military efficiency. It can legitimately demand that the scientific curriculum throughout all stages of education should be adequate and should be framed so as to give the best possible understanding of nature and man's place in nature, of the social functions of science and of its intellectual and practical importance. It can legitimately insist on large-scale educational campaigns outside the school and university system to help the general population to understand the value and importance of science as a whole or of this or that branch of scientific work, or to make people feel that they are actively and intelligently participating in the nation's scientific effort. It can legitimately do everything in its power to check superstition, to combat unscientific or anti-scientific attitudes of mind, and to promote an understanding of scientific method, of its value and importance.

Probably all men of science would agree that it is

legitimate, and most of them that it is desirable, for a Government to embark on such a policy. But they would assuredly only agree on certain conditions. In the first place, they would say that a government [1] has no right to pronounce in any way on the truth or falsity of any scientific facts, laws or theories, nor to exert pressure in favour of their acceptance or rejection by scientists. It must not subordinate the intellectual autonomy of science to any other criteria, whether religious, philosophical, or political, nor seek to impose upon scientific truth standards other than its own, nor relate scientific activity to any orthodoxy or authoritarian principle, nor, most of all, impose a scientific orthodoxy.

As implication of this, it must consult scientific opinion in forming its scientific policy, and leave all essentially scientific decisions in the hands of men of science. On the educational side of its scientific policy, it must, of course, consult educationalists as well as scientists, and recognize their autonomy in their own sphere.

It must recognize the special characteristics of science and the scientific method—the fact that it is essentially a universal activity ; that for its advance it depends very largely on freedom of publication, which in its turn implies freedom for other scientists to test and re-test published conclusions ; that major advances in scientific knowledge cannot be planned to order, and that new possibilities of practical advance often derive from the most unexpected quarters, including investigations undertaken with no practical aim.

[1] This applies equally to the political organisation in a one-party State (for example, the Communist Party in the U.S.S.R.), which in some respects is supra-governmental.

As a consequence of these characteristics of science, the State should permit the utmost freedom of publication consonant with military security ; it should encourage the international exchange of publications and research workers to the fullest extent ; and it should not insist on all research, even all research paid for out of Government funds, being directed to immediate practical objectives, but should leave a considerable " unplanned sector " of fundamental research to the free choice of the pure scientist.

In education, while not in any way minimizing the importance of science as an organised body of tested knowledge, it should also recognize the value of the scientific method—of free inquiry and free discussion, with reference back to fact where possible, as against dogmatic assertion and unreflective assimilation.

Meanwhile, I would suggest that scientists in general, and biologists in particular, have a responsibility in seeing that the great generalizations of modern genetics and evolutionary biology, which have so many important implications in so many fields, should be admitted as an indispensable part of general education.

It is unfortunately true that biology is rarely utilized as it might be in education, to provide future citizens with some of their most important guiding ideas. The biological curriculum in western countries often consists of a hotch-potch of disconnected subjects—a little nature study, a little human physiology and hygiene, a little zoology based mainly on the dissection of selected animal types, some botany, based largely on simple experiments in plant physiology, together with floral structure and the examination of a few major plant types, sometimes a little ecology (usually only plant ecology), and sometimes elementary Mendelism thrown in as an extra. In Britain, a great part of biological education at the secondary level is devoted to pre-medical work, and the syllabuses are largely coloured by the medical point of view and the requirements of medical students.

Even where there is an attempt to give a broader course and to treat biology as part of a general education, the result is often a diffuse and patchy collection of bits and pieces, many of them of great interest and importance, but not organized to give a unified picture of the world of life, its meaning and place in the general scheme of things, its significance for man and its relation to human affairs.

This appears to be due to a neglect of the concept and principles of evolution. It is a strange and lamentable fact that, although the theory of evolution is admittedly one of the greatest achievements of science, yet today, nearly a century after the publication of Darwin's great work, evolution has still, in our western countries, not found its proper place in general education. Sometimes it has not found its way into education at all ; and even when it has done so, it is almost invariably treated as a restricted and isolated topic, instead of a central idea. We have the strange fact that, although evolution is without question one of the major unifying concepts in general thought, it has not been used as one of the major unifying concepts of educationalists, or as one of the major unifying themes in general education.

Undoubtedly this is due in part to obstruction and prejudice, not only from religious bodies, but also from the upholders of traditional classical and humanistic systems. It has been said that it is also due partly to the difficulty of teaching the subject properly. This, however, can no longer be maintained, now that we have a coherent system of evolutionary theory based on neo-Mendelism and neo-Darwinism, and capable of giving ordered significance to the huge mass of evolutionary facts amassed by paleontologists, systematists, physiologists, zoologists, and botanists since Darwin's time.

This does not mean that we should start at the bottom, from the principles and laws of neo-Mendelian genetics and of Natural Selection, and thence work outwards and upwards by logical steps to the more discursive details of botany and zoology, any more than that, on the physico-chemical side of scientific education, we should start by trying to teach children the principles and laws of atomic physics and then work up to the more concrete realities of heat and light, mechanics and electricity. In physics and chemistry, however, the educationalists do have certain general principles in mind, they use them as an invisible framework for their curricula, and these curricula are formed so as to lead up to an eventual understanding of the principles. I think of such general principles as the conservation of matter and energy, the particulate structure of matter, the laws of radiation, of mass action, and so forth. In a general education, it is not possible to deal adequately with the more difficult problems of the subject—say, quantum theory or relativity—but curricula are, I repeat, usually drawn up with a coherent body of principles in mind, and with the design of making as much as possible of those principles explicit in the course of education.

Above all, the coherent body of principles makes it possible for the educationalist himself to have not only a coherent but a unifying approach and point of view. In physico-chemical science, that unifying point of view is a realization of the orderliness and inter-relatedness of all the phenomena of inorganic nature, however disorderly and however disparate they may at first sight appear. Thunder as a result of electric discharge in the atmosphere : heat as a mode of motion : the diversity of chemical substances as a result of different combinations of atoms : the move-ment of the planets as a special phenomenon of mechanics : colours as a result of radiation of different wave-lengths;—with the aid of our general principles the apparently chaotic facts are seen as parts of an orderly whole. And of course this general point of view has an important corollary or extension—namely that knowledge is power, and scientific understanding leads to practical control.

It is this unifying point of view which the teacher of physics and chemistry is able to put across, and the acquisition of some such general point of view is every whit as important as the learning of concrete facts and detailed laws.

In the same sort of way, the educationalist should have certain general principles at the back of his mind in framing and teaching the biological curriculum. Self-reproduction as the essential characteristics of living matter, together with the methods and principles of reproduction, sexual and asexual ; the particulate nature of inheritance ; the normal self-reproduction of the units of inheritance, together with their occasional mutation; their situation in the chromosomes; the resultant principles of neo-Mendelism. Natural Selec-tion as a consequence of self-reproduction and muta-tion; the various types and methods of selection ;

evolution as a consequence of Natural Selection. Evolution as an irreversible process, and one generating novelty ; evolutionary change of various kinds—specialization, degeneration, progress. Psychological principles in biology ; the mental component or aspect of evolution ; the evolution of mind ; human development and history as a continuation of biological evolution, but operating with different methods and different types of result, and on an accelerated time-scale—these are some of the ideas that should be in his mind.

The unifying point of view behind these principles is that life is an orderly, continuous and irreversible process, including mental (psychological) as well as material (physico-chemical) factors. [1]

This curt statement demands a little amplification. In the first place, we are enabled to realize that biological phenomena are just as orderly and as capable of being interpreted in naturalistic and scientific terms as are physico-chemical phenomena. Secondly, however, biology is more comprehensive than physico-chemical science, since it includes mental as well as material components ; in biology, mind is a proper subject for scientific study, and through biology mind

[1] Of course the mental components or factors of biological phenomena are clearly distinguishable only in the later stages of animal evolution, but this does not reduce their importance. It is not possible in the present state of our knowledge to say with certainty whether mind, as we know or deduce it, is a wholly novel emergent in evolution, or whether it is the result of a gradual development from a more primitive mind-like or ' mentoid ' property of all life, although on the principle of continuity and that of William of Occam's Razor the latter view is the simpler. This, however, is irrelevent to the general thesis, which is that, when we look at life—the subject-matter of biology—in the only correct way, as a unitary process, we find that mental or psychological phenomena are an integral part of the process, and in its later stages constitute an important part of its operating mechanism, finally becoming man's most important aspect.

becomes admissible as a part of scientific reality. And thirdly, biological phenomena can only be properly understood in dynamic terms. Life is a process, the process that is technically styled organic evolution. The course of the process follows certain rules and laws, and it is operated by certain mechanisms (notably Natural Selection working by way of neo-Mendelian inheritance). Thus the over-all aim of biology is to understand the process of evolution.

In so far as we understand the process of evolution, we can begin to control certain aspects of evolution. We can also reach a fuller understanding of the various special fields of biology if we think of them not as neither separate nor static, but as interrelated parts of the dynamic whole, the evolutionary process. A morphological " type " for instance, such as the frog, almost universally dedicated to zoological syllabuses, however interesting in itself, takes on new layers of significance as it is regarded from the angle of its behaviour and the type of experience of which it is capable, of its past development and future reproduction, of its past and possible future evolutionary history, of its relationships with the other members of its ecological community, which are themselves both individually and collectively the products of evolution.

With such a body of principles and such a general point of view in mind, the biological educationalist can fruitfully frame a syllabus which will treat the most important aspects of his science. The main types of animals and plants ; the main types of physiology of higher animals, higher plants, bacteria, etc. ; methods of reproduction and development ; parasitism, pests, disease and hygiene ; ecology ; animal behaviour ; adaptation ; histology and cytology ; genetics ;

Natural Selection and its modes of action ; elementary paleontology ; species and species-formation, with elementary systematics ; the course of Evolution, including the differentiation of major and minor groups, long-range trends, extinction, evolutionary progress ; animal societies ; the origin of man and human society ; the basic differences between biological and human (social) evolution.[1]

With such a general point of view behind them, these different fields of biology need no longer weigh on the pupil's mind as so many separate lumps of disconnected fact, but can be seen as various aspects of the single evolutionary process, and in so doing become more easily assimilable. Furthermore, biology itself need no longer be regarded as a subject for specialists, as an unfortunate pre-requisite for a medical career, or as a disagreeable extra tacked on to an already overloaded curriculum. It can take its place as one half of the general education in science which should be taken by all ; and, since it deals with the evolution both of matter and of mind, it can serve as an educational bridge between physico-chemical science and the humanities. It will also help to dissipate the present widespread ignorance of biological principles, which in its turn is taken advantage of by interested parties to prevent socially desirable applications of

[1] At Grammar School level in Britain, the better schools have accomplished a good deal towards giving effect to such an evolutionary approach to biology ; but a great deal remains to be done, both at this and other levels of the educational system. For instance, many Universities still lag behind in this respect.

It should be pointed out that the Russians do insist on a unified point of view in biological education. Michurinism is now to be taught in all schools and universities (see above ; and Kaptanov, 1948). The west needs to consolidate its own scientific position through its educational system.

biology or (as in the U.S.S.R.) to distort scientific truth for ideological reasons.

Biologists should not be content until the results of their labours are incorporated in some such way as this in the educational system of their countries. Only so can they be assured of general lay support for their research work, and of the atmosphere of opinion in which their science can develop freely and find full and fruitful application.

The State must recognize that science has an autonomous aspect. In the first place, it is a quest for knowledge and understanding of nature as well as a means of controlling it, and some of the most valuable discoveries have been made by men completely unconcerned with possible practical importance, and interested only in discovery for its own sake. In the second place, although scientific progress is obviously conditioned by its social and economic environment, it is not wholly determined by them. Granted that scientific activity is maintained at or above a certain level, it has a certain momentum of its own, which will automatically lead to the clarification of fields whose exploration has begun. [1]

I would suggest that the time is propitious—and also pressing—for men of science and of goodwill all over the world to unite in thinking out these problems and in particular in defining the scope and degree of the autonomy of science in relation to other higher activities of man, to politics, and to the State. The final outcome should be a public statement, brief yet comprehensive, a profession of scientific faith, an affirmation of the rights and duties of science and of scientists.

[1] Dr. J. R. Baker has directed my attention to the fact that the above suggestions are much along the lines of those put forward by the Society for Freedom in Science during the past nine years.

208

In framing this, should not the leading role be taken by the premier national scientific bodies? Thus, in Britain, we might hope that the Royal Society would take the responsibility. It would presumably wish to consult other bodies which have paid special attention to the subject, such as the Society for Freedom in Science, and would doubtless secure much support from other national societies, such as the British Association and the Association of Scientific Workers, from regional bodies like the Royal Society of Edinburgh, and from the Institutes and Societies concerned with particular branches of science, especially those dealing with genetics and evolutionary biology.

To put the matter on an international basis, the International Council of Scientific Unions should be called upon, which would then make contact with its various constituent Unions, and with international professional bodies such as the International Federation of Scientific Workers.

A manifesto of this kind, subscribed to by the greatest possible number of scientific organisations and societies, would be a powerful instrument of scientific freedom and an affirmation of the supra-national and universal character of scientific activity.[1]

The converse of this should also be undertaken, namely, the formulation of an international charter for science by the inter-governmental agencies concerned—Unesco in the lead, with the co-operation and agreement of the other specialized agencies concerned (notably F.A.O. and W.H.O.) and of the Economic and Social Council of the United Nations.

[1] I understand that the American Institute of Biological Science has prepared such a statement which was published in *Science*, Aug. 29, 1949.

In this, the Governments concerned would guarantee certain rights to science and to scientists, while presumably at the same time defining certain duties and responsibilities expected from them.

The third and quite specific question remains—how to persuade the U.S.S.R., together with any other countries which may be concerned, to alter its present policy towards science. Clearly nothing can be done here save by way of precept—through an inter-governmentally agreed charter as suggested above —and of persuasion—through a joint approach of the scientific academies of the rest of the world, and perhaps through the International Scientific Unions. In the particular case of genetics, a joint approach might be made by the specialized societies concerned with genetics and evolution, perhaps with the co-operation of the International Genetics Congress and the International Union of Biological Sciences. Any such approaches should lay strong emphasis on the unity and international character of science, as well as on the necessity for scientific freedom and autonomy *vis-a-vis* political or philosophical orthodoxy. Even though an effort of this sort is unlikely to be effective, there is perhaps a duty to make it.

Meanwhile, there is a great deal to be done in our own countries towards securing a better general understanding of the questions involved, both the specific issues of the Lysenko controversy, and the more general question of the nature and role of scientific method.

This applies to professional scientists as well as to laymen. Thus Professor J. D. Bernal, in a letter to the *Manchester Guardian* (February 4, 1949), writes " I do not consider that any ' terrible injury to the freedom and integrity of science ' has been done in the Soviet Union. On the contrary, I think that the discussions that are going on there in biology and physics are signs of new and fundamentally healthy tendencies of criticizing the theoretical foundations of science and of bringing experimental science into closer relations with current human activities and needs . . . A new people require and will find a new theoretical basis for the whole of their science." Professor Bernal appears to ignore the function of science devoted to providing knowledge irrespective of the social needs of the time ; and also the conditions of freedom necessary for the successful operation of the scientific method. If a party line is laid down, directing what facts and ideas are to be accepted and what rejected, what lines of research are to be pursued and what are not permitted—is that not an injury to the freedom of science ? And the discussion was *not* limited to theoretical criticism—it involved the rejection of established facts and laws, and the branding of all science in foreign countries as hostile and wrong.

At one of the banquets during the Academy celebrations in Moscow in 1945, after I had heard Lysenko's lecture, I sat next to a well-known and distinguished Russian physicist, who asked me what I thought of Lysenko. On my replying that I thought that his theories were scientifically nonsense, and that his factual claims were both exaggerated and unproven, he replied in rather a shocked voice that this *couldn't* be so. So far as I could make out, he felt that a man who had reached a position of such eminence and power must be scientifically competent. This illustrates the difficulties raised by the specialization of modern science. It is extremely difficult for a man in one branch of science to pronounce on the importance and validity of new ideas in another branch. On the other hand, he can find out whether research and discussion have been carried on in a scientific way and subject to the usual scientific criteria, though this will normally take a good deal of time and trouble. But when the issues are as important as they are in the genetics controversy, it may be his duty to give up time and energy to such a task.

On the other hand, it is true that many men of science in Western countries still seem to believe that science can and should operate in what I may call a social vacuum, and others adopt a laisser-faire attitude as regards the social functions of science. They too should take the time and trouble to think out what are and should be the relations between science and society.

This applies equally to the general public, only what is demanded of many of them is something wider—to clear their minds about the nature of scientific method in general.

Bernard Shaw in a recent article (1949) supports Lysenko and the action of the U.S.S.R. Academy of Sciences on the ground that neo-Darwinism is fatalism or determinism and that " it becomes plain at once that it is a doctrine that no State can tolerate, least of all a Socialist State, in which every citizen shall aim at altering circumstance for the better purposely and conscientiously, and no criminal militant reactionary can be excused on the ground that his actions are not his own. . . ." Later he states that " the real issue is between the claim of the scientific profession to be exempted from all legal restraint in the pursuit of knowledge, and the duty of the State to control it in the general interest as it controls all other pursuits."

Mr. Shaw here reveals his customary incomprehension of the nature and methods of science (I heard him once at a luncheon girding at scientists : "they tell us that the sun is 90 million miles away. How do they know ? They haven't been there " !). Even if neo-Darwinism did encourage a fatalistic philosophy, which it does not, this would not make it untrue, or condone the State's vetoing it to teachers or research workers. Nor does Lamarckism become fact because Mr. Shaw and the U.S.S.R. Academy of Sciences feel that it would be nice if it were true.

He confuses the issue over the question of legal restraint, for in regard to this he adduces the right of the State to prevent a man of science from boiling his mother " to ascertain at what temperature a mature woman will die." Of course, the State has the right to limit and regulate research (as, for example, by means of laws and regulations concerning vivisection) ; but what is here at stake is something quite different—the right of the State to reject scientifically ascertained facts and to brand whole branches of science as false or not permissible.

Let me give further illustrations of the need for clear thinking about science, from the correspondence about the genetics controversy. Here are some points from letters in the *Saturday Review of Literature* for May 7, 1949, concerning the articles of Professor Muller and George Bernard Shaw. " Muller is inconsistent when he claims for himself the right to criticize the exercise of power by governments," But Muller was not criticizing the exercise of power by governments. He was saying that the exercise of authoritarian power by governments to secure rejection of scientific theories, still more of scientific facts, is incompatible with scientific advance.

" Must readers accept Muller's statement that the findings of geneticists such as Scheinfeld and Altenburg are so recondite that even exemplification is out of the question ? Is their curiosity about genetic research never to be even partially satisfied unless the sacred text of the geneticists' actual words is perused reverentially ? " This correspondent has made the mistake— alas, all too common !—of ascribing statements to his adversary which he never made. What Muller wrote was that " neither public platforms nor non-technical periodicals are suitable for the exposition of these facts [the detailed facts gained by genetic research], for the public has not the patience to be bothered with the intricacies. However, there are a few sound lay treatment, such as Scheinfeld's " You and Heredity " or Altenburg's " How we inherit," and there are good brief presentation in several modern high school and college texts."

As any teacher of biology knows, it takes weeks or months of lectures and demonstrations and exercises to give an averagely intelligent student a reasonable understanding of the facts and theories of genetics. In printed form, a small book is the minimum requirement. How can the necessary mass of facts and background ideas be conveyed in the course of a short popular article ?

I open a textbook of genetics at random and find the following statement : " When a fly with the three sex-linked genes rb (ruby eye-color), ct (cut wings), and v (vermilion eye-color) is crossed with a wild-type fly with the dominant allelomorphs of these genes, and the F_1 heterozygous females are crossed with the triply recessive type, the following results are obtained . . . non-crossovers, 1,129 ; single crossovers, 478 ; double crossovers, 15." This deals merely with one aspect of linkage : but to render it intelligible to someone without any genetical training it would have to be expanded to cover several pages. Why should the layman expect that genetics is any easier to explain briefly in words of one syllable than the quantum theory, say, or the differential calculus ?

Again, another correspondent writes that Muller states that Shaw and Lysenko " would not accept "the facts of genetics. What Muller wrote was " We cannot argue profitably with Lysenko on the subject, any more than we could have argued profitably with William Jennings Bryan or the fanatical preacher Henry Norris, because their statements show them to be ignorant and hopelessly confused as to those facts, while able to put up a shifting front that readily deceives the uninitiated." This is unfortunately all too true. I myself found it impossible to argue scientifically with Lysenko, because, as I have said, he doesn't talk the same language as I do, because he doesn't observe the rules of the scientific game, and because he is thinking in terms of preconceived doctrine or dogma, not in terms of reference back to scientific fact.

Another correspondent :—" Controversial scientists make little progress unless they understand that their pronouncements are only tentative and may be strengthened or destroyed by future data ... No personal emotion should be involved no matter how dear to the heart of Dr. Muller his own theory may be." This involves a really serious misconception—the conception that science is all a matter of pronouncements and theories. Science consists of an ever-increasing body of established factual knowledge, together with a set of ideas for interpreting that knowledge. The ideas may be rejected, but the facts cannot. Muller was not being controversial as a scientist, for he was not arguing about " his own theory " : he was reminding his readers that genetics is, among other things, an established body of scientific fact. As for emotion, I would say that it is the duty of the scientist to feel strongly about truth. If he did not, he would probably not become a scientist at all, and certainly not a good scientist. When truth is attacked or suppressed, it is his duty to speak out.

Finally, I will quote various points from a letter in the *New Statesman* of September 25, 1948.

(1) " The orthodox geneticists have long maintained that the potentialities of the germ-plasm are congenital, innate, and unchangeable by circumstance." This is incorrect. They have *established* that the *material basis* of the germ-plasm is unchangeable (except by mutation). They would all agree that the *potentialities* of the germ-plasm are " changeable by circumstance," the same genes in one set of circumstances giving rise to one character, in another set of circumstances to another (as with the colour of the legs of fowls, previously cited).

(2) He then refers to this as a *premise*. It is not a premise, but a basis of fact.

(3) " Such a theory can be used to justify passive acceptance of the working of chance, and it is as ' scientific fatalism ' that it has been attacked ". (*a*) It is not a theory, but a set of facts. (*b*) It *has* been attacked as ' scientific fatalism ' ; but an elementary understanding of the nature of science should be sufficient to remind us that the scientific value of facts and theories cannot legitimately be attacked on such ideological grounds.

(4) " In animal breeding . . . the points at issue are
(i) whether *all* characters are ' fixed ' at birth." Very
few characters are ' fixed ' at birth : all characters
depend on the interaction between genes and environment during development. Apparently, the writer is
again confusing *character* with *hereditary factor*.

(5) " Lysenko appears to maintain (1) that only
certain socially irrelevant characters (such as pigmentation) are innate ; and (2) that other characters are
modifiable in infancy and childhood . . . Obviously
this theory is of great importance with regard, for
example, to the " congenital " diseases hitherto regarded as transmissible . . . Lysenko's theory means
that the child of tubercular parents need not have
tubercular children."

I am not at all sure that Lysenko would agree with
this formulation of his views. But it is true that he
merely *maintains* this position—it is a mere hypothesis,
not an established fact.

In any case, some diseases *are* transmissible (hemo-
philia, for instance) ; but no geneticist ever maintained
that the child of tubercular parents must needs have
tubercular children, though some individuals are
genetically more prone to tuberculosis than others.

(6) " Possibly the ' orthodox geneticists ' would not
deny this ; but if, then, they rest their case solely on
the transmission of such characters as pigmentation,
which no one in their senses could consider as socially
important, their science is of negligible social utility,
and this is precisely the charge against the Vavilov
school."

Why do people not take the trouble to look up a few
facts ? If this correspondent had consulted any textbook of genetics, he would have seen that the ' orthodox

geneticists' have established that all (or almost all) characters of all (or almost all) organisms depend on genes. They rest their case on scientific fact : the social utility of genetics depends on what use the facts of science are put to.

In any case, he betrays no sign of having realized that science is not a matter of advancing or maintaining ideas, or of making pronouncements, but of establishing a body of tested facts and concepts.

Too many people fail to distinguish between fact, hypothesis, theory, doctrine, and dogma ; too many seem to equate pronouncement with proof. Too few understand the nature of the scientific method, and the conditions it needs in order to flourish and give fruitful results.

An extraordinary statement was made in the British Communist Party's " Educational Commentary on Current Affairs "(1), which stated that " the essential point of controversy between those who think like Lysenko, and the orthodox geneticists was : whether or not the hereditary nature of living organisms can be changed ; whether or not man can alter existing species of animals or plants by his action, and whether he can succeed in producing new types of plants and animals suited to his needs." This is either an example of unpardonable scientific ignorance, or else a deliberate misstatement. Every ' orthodox geneticist ' knows that the hereditary nature of living organisms can be changed—otherwise there could be no evolution—and can give numerous examples of man having produced new types of plants and animals suited to his needs— Darwin wrote two volumes on the subject. The point at issue is not whether the hereditary nature of organisms can be changed, but solely the method by which that change is brought about.

As Cook (1949) writes, "All too often . . . we are still tempted to ascribe to science and the scientist the idea of the priest and the magician." This misconception of the nature of science leads people to take the opinions of scientists as authoritative pronouncements of dogmatic truth, whereas the only authority is that of scientific fact.

At the opposite extreme are those who, having realized that scientific method demands a suspension of judgment, and that scientific theories are constantly changing, dispute the right of the scientist to speak with any special authority, and indeed challenge any idea of scientific certitude.

But science is not magic ; nor is it just a set of constantly changing ideas. It is a process for arriving at a constantly increasing body of established truth. The increase is both in the extent and the accuracy of what is established. That truth is never absolute nor can the body of scientific truth ever be complete ; but what does exist is established as fact. Scientific theories inevitably change, for they include interpretation as well as fact, and the interpretation may have to be altered as new facts are discovered. But a change in theory does not alter the facts and laws already established, as I have already pointed out with regard to the extreme case provided by the supersession of classical physical theory by the theory of relativity.

On the other hand, the facts and laws are merely statements of the results of our observations and experiments on nature ; so their accuracy can be and is constantly being improved. Science itself is thus an apparently contradictory blend of certitude and incertitude. But the apparent contradiction is resolved once it is realized that science is a process. It is the increase of tested knowledge, and not a body of absolute truth, nor yet merely a constantly changing set of new techniques.

The geneticist has every right to say with authority that genes exist and segregate—those are established facts. He has no right to say that our present knowledge of genes and their behaviour is complete. He also has every right to say that no one has any scientific right to disregard the facts which genetics science has established. Even if some new theoretical interpretation proves to be required, it cannot start from far behind the present front of science, as Lysenko does, but must take account of existing knowledge.

Science in the modern sense is a very recent development, less than four centuries old. It is a special branch of human activity, devoted to increasing our knowledge of natural phenomena and our control over them. To do this it must adopt certain methods, the most important of which is the constant reference back to natural fact. Neither authority nor unaided reason is sufficient. Scientific knowledge must be public knowledge, in the philosophical sense—that is, it must be capable of being checked by any others who have acquired the necessary skill and experience and techniques. To facilitate such checking, it is not enough for a research worker to publish merely his results and conclusions : he must also publish an account of the data from which he drew his conclusions and the methods which he used to obtain the data. Discussion, at scientific societies, international scientific congresses and small *ad hoc* groups of scientists, is also a fruitful method for permitting scientists to become acquainted with each other's techniques and criticisms.

Wherever it is possible, controlled experiment is the

best way of arriving at new knowledge, and the technique of experimentation has to be learnt like anything else. Where experiment is not possible, we must fall back on observation, and various procedures and precautions have been developed to ensure that the conclusions drawn from this shall be as firm as possible.

Experience has shown that scientific advance often comes from the most unlikely quarters, and that to try to dictate what subjects shall and shall not be investigated reduces the efficacy of science. From the outset, modern science has been international. All major development in science have been due to contributions from hundreds of workers, in many countries ; and no research worker can afford to neglect the work of foreign scientists.

Science advances partly by framing scientific laws ; these are general statements embodying or subsuming particular bodies of scientific fact. It also advances by the setting up of hypotheses which are afterwards tested against fact by means of observation or experiment. Many hypotheses have to be abandoned as incorrect, while the correct ones become incorporated into broad scientific theories. These are not mere speculations, but general ideas which take account of (and in a sense incorporate) large bodies of scientific fact and the scientific laws subsuming these facts.

Ideas that were perfectly legitimate as one stage of scientific development may be completely out-dated by the advance of knowledge, so that they become mere superstitions. This is true to-day for instance of the idea of spontaneous generation, out-dated by the work of Pasteur and his successors, or of the geocentric theory of the universe, disproved by Copernicus and Galileo, or of the idea that existing kinds of animals and plants were specially created, out-dated by Darwin. Most biologists would say that crude ideas of the inheritance of acquired characters, like those of Lamarck or Lysenko, had now been so out-dated by Mendel, Morgan and modern genetics as to have become superstitions instead of legitimate scientific hypotheses.

Science cannot flourish and cannot be fully fruitful save in certain material conditions and in a certain moral and intellectual atmosphere. As Muller (1949) well puts it, " It has taken thousands of years to build the basis of that freedom of inquiry and of criticism which science requires. It has been possible only through the growth of democratic practices, and through the associated progress in physical techniques, in living standards, and in education, applied on a grand scale. Only in modern times have all these conditions advanced sufficiently to permit the widespread, organized, objective search for truth which we to-day think of when we use the word Science."

But the atmosphere necessary for science to flourish can be all too readily destroyed or poisoned, whether by ignorance and mental laziness, by prejudice and vested interests, or by authoritarian power.

Scientific advance has constantly met with resistances. We are all familiar with the resistance put up by religious orthodoxy or religious prejudice to astronomical advance in the time of Galileo, or to biological advance in the time of Darwin. But such incidents may be regarded as particular examples of the general conflict between society as a continuing organization and science as an innovator of ideas and techniques, which is still very much with us to-day.

It is often difficult for the individual to jettison the

ideas in which he has been brought up, and in which he has constructed his picture of reality and his role in the world. But the conflict is more serious on the social than on the individual plane.

Darlington (1948 bis) in his pamphlet *The Conflict Between Science and Society* has discussed this problem at some length. There is a real conflict between the claims of stability and those of change. Too rapid change may lead to disruption ; too great stability will stand in the way of desirable improvement. Somehow we must arrive at a working compromise which will permit an optimum or at least a reasonable rate of change. But we should not allow unreasonable and unreasoning prejudice or unscientific authoritarianism to provide the brake on progress. To achieve this, education is needed—education of political leaders as well as of the public at large—to make people aware of the social process as evolution, of the necessity of enlisting science in the service of that process, and of the immense possibilities of new knowledge, new directives, and new control implicit in the full utilization of the scientific method.

Hogben (1949) has drawn attention to other dangers threatening the advance of scientific discovery, inherent in the development of large-scale organization in scientific research, which tend to reduce scientific freedom and initiative and to increase the degree of non-scientific control of science.

All such dangers are most acute in a society which is governed on authoritarian principles. Lord Acton's famous dictum, " Power corrupts, and absolute power corrupts absolutely," has received new confirmation in modern authoritarian States, such as Nazi Germany and in Soviet Russia, especially in its later develop-

ment. If men are convinced that they are right and if
at the same time they have the power to enforce their
convictions, the temptation to abandon tolerance and
suppress scientific freedom becomes difficult to resist.
Only by bitter experience are authoritarian states
likely to learn the lesson that such suppression is in the
long run disastrous. The actions and the methods of
Lysenko and of the Academy of Science and the
Communist Party in the U.S.S.R. in supporting him
are in my view intellectually and socially deplorable.
But if the issues of principle which they have raised are
clearly grasped and taken to heart, and the conclusions
from them resolutely drawn, the battle of Soviet
genetics will not have been fought and lost in vain.
For this will mean that the scientific movement will
for the first time become fully conscious of itself
and of its social function ; and it will also mean that the
western world will have a better appreciation of the
nature and methods of science, of its functions as a new
tool in humanity's hands, of its potentialities for men's
further progress, of the vital importance but at the same
time the limitations of scientific method, of the equal
importance of a proper degree of scientific autonomy,
and of the rights and duties of science in relation to
other higher activities of man, to the State, and to
human society as a whole.

When this book was already in proof, two important articles on the genetics controversy by two distinguished British scientists sympathetic to communism were published in the Modern Quarterly (Vol. 4, No. 3)— " In Defence of Genetics " by the geneticist Professor J. B. S. HALDANE, F.R.S., and " The Biological Controversy in the Soviet Union and its Implications " by the crystallographer and physicist Professor J. D. BERNAL, F.R.S.

Professor Haldane does not deal with what I consider the main issue, namely the official banning of Mendelian genetics on the basis of a scientific party line. He is only concerned with an appraisal of the views of Lysenko and his followers (which, he points out, " has been made much more difficult by ill-informed criticism of [Mendelian] genetics by supporters of Lysenko in this country " [Britain].

He says that Lysenko's speech made him realize for the first time " the idealistic character of Mendel's formulation of his results," because Mendel had spoken of the transmission in heredity of " differentiating characters " (as opposed to genetic units). However, whether on this point MENDEL was or was not under the influence of Thomist philosophy, as Haldane suggests, is irrelevant to the situation today (as Haldane himself later implies). Geneticists quite early realized the illegitimacy of speaking of the inheritance of *characters* (except as an occasional form of convenient short-hand) and began talking in terms of the inheritance of *hereditary factors*—which were later styled *genes*.

He is also critical of the *mechanist* tendencies of some neo-Mendelians. However, on the scientific issue he takes his stand unequivocally in favour of neo-Mendelism and neo-Darwinism. " I am a Mendelist-Morganist, although Mendel used an idealist terminology, and Morgan wrote of the machanism of heredity. But Morgan and his colleagues made the very great advance of showing that heredity has a material, not a metaphysical basis."

He accepts the fact of the existence of genes, and the general theory of the gene. " We do not cease to believe in atoms because they can be split. Nor need we cease to believe in genes because they can be changed. On the contrary, if they were unchangeable, I, as a Marxist, could not believe in them."

" In a recent discussion in London, some Marxists went so far as to deny that there was a material basis of inheritance. There is good reason to doubt that any parts of a cell are *only* the material basis of heredity. Genes certainly play an active part in a cell's ordinary life. But a Marxist can no more deny a material basis for heredity than for sensation or thought."

I am extremely glad that Haldane has made this statement. But it is worth pointing out that many of the speakers on Lysenko's side in the discussion did deny the existence of genes, or their significance as a material basis for heredity ; and it is worth wondering what would have happened if Haldane had made these same statements in Moscow during the session of the Academy of Agricultural Science.

Haldane also affirms the Mendelian interpretation of the value of wide crosses, though he adds that these not only produce new combinations of genes of pre-existing type, but changes to genes of new type. He is also " sceptical of the claims that in general ' acquired characters are inherited ' " (though he considers that Lysenko's claim to have converted spring wheats into autumn wheats is established).

Elsewhere he says " it must be realized that the results of experimental work are not available until they are published in such a form that they can be repeated." This is an unobtrusive and indirect way of drawing attention to the unscientific procedure of the Michurinites in not publishing their results in an adequate way. He concludes by saying that " Marxist circles " have made " wholly unjustifiable attacks " on the profession of genetics.

Professor Bernal, on the other hand, when he is not dragging in subjects which have nothing to do with the genetical issue, such as the purely agrological successes of the Soviet regime (e.g., in regard to forest shelter-belts, soil-conservation, etc.), is concerned with the Marxist thesis (of which he approves) that new social conditions are bound to give rise to new kinds of scientific theories, and indeed to new kinds of science. On this basis, he defends the views and actions of the Michurinites, and justifies the drawing of a distinction between bourgeois and Soviet science.

I cannot attempt to summarize his lengthy, learned, and ingenious article, but must content myself by saying that I consider that he has unfairly evaded the major issues, of the legitimacy of officially condemning a whole branch of science as false, anti-scientific, anti-patriotic, etc., and of the scientific validity of the results obtained and the methods employed by the Michurinites. It is a specious, if brilliant, piece of apologetics, not an impartial discussion.

I will take one example. In one place he writes,

" genetics seem due for a change, and that change will have to be fairly fundamental, if it is to act at the same time as an explanation for observed effects and as a stimulus to acquire and use new ones." Elsewhere he states that Lysenko " clearly wishes to make the most use possible of the methods and data that have been accumulated." This last statement is in flat contradiction with Lysenko's own statements on neo-Mendelian data, many of which I have cited in this book, and is not easily to be reconciled with the out-and-out condemnation of the whole system of neo-Mendelism (" pseudo-scientific Morgano-Weismannite tendency," etc.) in the resolutions of the Academy of Sciences cited in Chapter 2, or with the exhortations of Lysenko, Prezent, and others to combat neo-Mendelism as unpatriotic, ideologically pernicious, and the enemy of genetic progress.

Nor is the official rejection of " Morgano-Mendelism" compatible with the statement made by Bernal that the radical development of genetic theory that he foresees will have to take account of already observed effects, since most of these have been contemptuously rejected by the Michurinites as untrue or misleading. The rejection of the entire theoretical framework of a science can hardly be described merely as a change, even " a fairly fundamental " change, in that science.

In general, I cannot see how new social conditions could do more than *condition* the growth of new theories, or new developments or new orientations of existing theories. But even if they could entirely *determine* such new growth or new orientation, it does not follow that the result would necessarily be good or the theory correct. If Professor Bernal were a geneticist instead of a physicist, he would realize that Lysenko's theories are, scientifically speaking, largely nonsense—meaning that they do not make scientific sense. They will have to undergo " a fairly fundamental change " before they can be regarded as scientific, and that change, if it ever occurs, will be brought about by the pressure of fact and scientific method, and must involve the re-acceptance of the facts of Mendelism which they have now scorned and rejected.

It must also be pointed out that neo-Mendelian genetics has a very favourable record of achievement and development as compared with Michurinism. All that Michurinism can show is a body of doctrine unrelated to any recent scientific advance, together with two new discoveries, neither of which has yet been proved valid.

On the other side, we have the discovery and analysis of the material basis of heredity ; the elucidation of the main mechanism of biological evolution ; the beginning of the physico-chemical exploration of the material basis of life itself. These are all achievements of neo-Mendelian genetics, taken in the natural stride of its development. Far from being in a state of " most unsatisfactory confusion," as Bernal asserts, classical genetics is in an extremely healthy and vigorous condition, and shows every sign of being able to cope satisfactorily with the numerous new developments to which it is giving rise.

POSTSCRIPT II

The following is a verbatim translation of Y. Zhdanov's letter to Stalin, as published in *Pravda* on August 7th, 1948.

Y. Zhdanov had recently been appointed a member of Section B of the Central Committee of the Communist Party, and was working in the science department. The letter was written to appear on the last day of the genetics discussion in the Academy of Agricultural Sciences, obviously with a view to regularizing Zhdanov's position vis-a-vis the new situation created by the laying down of an official party line in genetics.

" *To Comrade J. V. Stalin.*

" In a paper on controversial questions of contemporary Darwinism given at a school for lecturers, I certainly made quite a number of serious mistakes.

" 1. The very attitude of this paper was mistaken. I obviously underestimated my new position as a member of the Central Committee's staff, underestimated my responsibility, did not realize that my statement would be appraised as the official view of the C.C. What showed itself here was the ' university habit ' of not hesitating to express my own point of view in a scientific argument. So, when I was asked to read a paper at the school for lecturers, I decided to express my own ideas there too, stating the proviso that it was a ' personal point of view ' so that what I said should bind nobody to anything. Without a doubt, this is a ' professorial ' (in the bad sense) and not a Party position.

" 2. The radical mistake in the paper itself was its aim towards compromise between conflicting trends in biology.

" From the very first day of my work in the science department representatives of formal genetics began to come to me with complaints that new varieties of useful plants obtained by them (buckwheat, koksagys, geranium, hemp and citruses), possessing improved qualities, were not being introduced into production and were coming up against the opposition of Academician Lysenko's supporters. These undoubtedly useful forms of plants were obtained by direct action of chemical and physical factors on the germ cell (on the seeds). The Michurin teaching does not deny the possibility and appropriateness of such action, recognizing, however, the presence of many other, more important ways of changing the organism. Formal genetics considers its methods (severe shock to the organism by X-rays, ultra-violet rays, colchicine, acenapthene) as the only possible ones. I am aware that the mechanism of the action of these agents on the organism can and should be explained not by formal but by Michurin genetics.

" My mistake was that, having decided to take under protection these *practical* results, which were ' Danaan gifts ' (Trojan horse gifts—translator), I did not mercilessly criticise the radical methodological defects of Mendel-Morgan genetics. I recognize that this was the ' business ' approach to practical work, a hunt for ha'pence.

" The struggle of the trends in biology often assumes the distorted forms of squabbles and scandal. However, it seemed to me that in general there was nothing more in this than these squabbles and scandals. Consequently, I underestimated the principle contained in the matter, approached the dispute unhistorically, without having analysed its deep causes and roots.

" All this taken together produced the desire to ' reconcile ' the disputing sides, to wash out the disagreements, to emphasize that which unites and not that which separates the opponents. But in science, as in politics, principles are not subject to compromise, but gain victory ; struggle proceeds not by damping down but by disclosing contradictions. The attempt to make peace between principles on a ' business ' and narrowly practical basis, the underestimation of the theoretical side of the argument, led to eclecticism, which I admit.

" 3. My sharp and public criticism of Academician Lysenko was a mistake. Academician Lysenko is at the present time the recognized head of the Michurin trend in biology, he has defended Michurin and his teachings from attack by the bourgeois geneticists, and has himself done much for science and for the conduct of our economy. Bearing this in mind, criticism of Lysenko, of his particular deficiencies, should be so conducted as not to weaken but strengthen the position of the Michurinites.

" I do not agree with certain theoretical propositions of Academician Lysenko (denial of intra-species struggle and mutual aid, underestimation of the internal specific characters of the organism). I consider that he is still making poor use of the treasure-house of Michurin's teachings (it is for this very reason that Lysenko has not produced any significant varieties of agricultural plants). I consider that he is a poor leader of our agricultural science. The Lenin all-Union Academy of Agricultural Sciences, of which he is head, is working at far from its full capacity. It is doing nothing on animal husbandry, on the economics and organization of agriculture, and the way it tackles work on agro-culture is poor. But criticism of all these deficiencies should not be done in the way I did in my paper. As a result of my criticism of Lysenko the formal geneticists turned out to be the ' third party ' gainers.

" In my whole-hearted devotion to Michurin's teachings, I criticized Lysenko not for being a Michurinite but for insufficiently developing Michurin's teachings. However, the form of the criticism was chosen incorrectly. Therefore, objectively the Michuri-nites lost by such criticism and the Mendel-Morganites gained.

" 4. Lenin more than once pointed out that recog-nition of the necessity of some phenomenon carries with it the danger of falling into objectivism. To a certain degree, even I did not escape this danger.

" I characterized the place of Weismannism and Mendel-Morganism (I don't separate them) to a con-siderable extent in the manner of Fimen : taking the good and evil indifferently. Instead of coming down heavily on these anti-scientific views (expressed here by Schmalhausen and his school) which in theory are a veiled form of clericalism—theological concepts of the origin of species as the result of individual acts of creation, and which in practice lead to the ' limit feeling '—to denial of man's capacity to remake the nature of animals and plants, I mistakenly set myself the task of ' perceiving ' their place in the development of biological theory, to find the ' rational kernel ' in them. As a result, my criticism of Weismannism turned out to be weak, objectivist, and in effect—shallow.

In the upshot, again the main blow fell on Academi-cian Lysenko, that is, it ricochetted against Michurin.

" Such are my mistakes as I understand them.

" I consider it my duty to assure you, Comrade Stalin, and in your person the Central Committee of the C.P.S.U. (B), that I have been and remain an ardent Michurinite. My mistakes derive from an insufficient mastery of the history of the question, and from incorrect preparation of the front of struggle for Michurin's teachings. All this because of inexperience and immaturity. I will repair my mistakes in work.

" July 10th, 1948."   " YURI ZHDANOV."[1]

The letter deserves a few comments.

Section 2. Zhdanov seems to have been quite satisfied that the new types (mostly polyploids) produced by the neo-Mendelians were of practical value, in spite of the repeated assertions of Lysenko and his followers to the contrary.

His statement that the mechanism of the action of colchicine, etc., in inducing genetic change should be explained by Michurin and not by " formal " genetics is, to me at least, scientifically incomprehensible. The action of X-rays is due entirely to their effect on single genes or on the structure of chromosomes ; that of colchicine to its effect on the number of chromosomes—which are, after all, the basis of " formal genetics." It is impossible to see how Michurinism could advance a view which did not involve explanation in these terms.

His further statement, if it signifies anything more than an affirmation of his own orthodoxy, implies that he adopts the view that in science ideological " principle " is more important than correctness of facts.

Section 3. It is extremely interesting that he should

[1] Reprinted by permission from *Soviet Studies* (Glasgow) No. 2, 1949.

still criticize Lysenko's shortcomings, both theoretical and practical. It seems clear that all is not quite so well with Soviet agriculture, either on the genetical or the agrobiological side, as some non-Russian apologists would have us believe.

Section 4. Western scientists will find it very difficult to understand what Zhdanov can have in mind when he says that neo-Mendelian views " in theory are a veiled form of clericalism—theological concepts of the origin of species as the result of individual acts of creation." I, for one, must confess that I find the statement incomprehensible.

What is clear, however, is that Zhdanov has perceived the need to become himself less " objective " and more partisan in his scientific views.

LITERATURE CITED

A. SUMMARIES OR REPORTS OF DISCUSSIONS, ETC.
   1-4 concern the 1948 discussion at the Lenin Academy
       of Agricultural Sciences.

[1] " The Session of the Lenin Academy of Agricultural Science,
    1948," (English) Plant Breeding Abstracts, **18**, p. 642, 1949
    (also includes the resolution of the Academy of Sciences and
    other matter).

[2] " Une discussion scientifique en U.R.S.S." Europe (Paris),
    26, No. 33-34, 1948 (French), contains the report of the
    session summarized in (1) above, together with editorial
    comments and other articles.

[3] " The Situation in Biological Science." (Proceedings of the
    Lenin Academy of Agricultural Sciences, July 31 - August
    7, 1948, etc.). Verbatim report of the above session (English).
    Foreign Languages Publishing House, Moscow, 1949.

[4] Soviet Biology, etc. (English) mimeographed : (verbatim
    reports of some of the contributions to above discussion).
    Society for Cultural Relations with the U.S.S.R., London,
    49 pp.

[5] (Report on the conference on Genetics, Science, and Selection,
    held in Moscow in 1939), in Pod-Znamenem Marxisma
    (under the Banner of Marxism) 1939 (Russian). (Mimeo-
    graphed English version in the possession of the Society for
    Cultural Relations with the U.S.S.R.).

[6] Bulletin of Atomic Scientists, May and Aug-Sept, 1949. (The
    issues are devoted largely to a discussion of the genetics con-
    troversy, by various authors).

[7] Educational Commentary on Current Affairs for 3 . i . 1949
    (issued for the British Communist Party by the *Daily Worker*
    and the Marx Memorial Library). This issue is devoted to
    the genetics controversy.

[8] " The Soviet Union since World War II." Annals Amer.
    Acad. Polit. Soc. Sci., Vol. 263, May, 1949. (A symposium
    by various writers).

[9] " Speaking of Peace," report on Cultural and Sci. Conf. for
    World Peace, March, 1949. (N.Y. Nat. Coun. of Arts,
    Sciences and Professions).

B. INDIVIDUAL CONTRIBUTIONS

ASHBY, E. (1946). "Survey of Botany in the Soviet Union." Rep. 25th meeting Austr. and N.Z. Ass. Adv. Sci., Adelaide, 1946, p. 245.

ASHBY, E. (1947). "Scientist in Russia," London, Penguin Books, Ltd.

ASHBY, E. (1948). "Genetics in the Soviet Union." Nature, 162, p. 912.

CONNORS, C. H. (1922). "Peach Breeding, a summary of results." Proc. Amer. Soc. Hort. Sci., 16, p. 23.

COOK, R. C. (1949). "Lysenko's Wonderful Genetics" (important general summary, with valuable bibliography by M. Leikind.) J. Hered 40, p. 367 (abridged in S.C.I. Monthly 68, June 1949.

CRANE, M. B. (1949a). "Lysenko on Grafting and Genetics." Discovery, 10 (2), p. 64.

CRANE, M. B. (1949b). "The Situation in Biological Science" (review of ³). Heredity, 3 (2).

DALE, H. H. (1949). Discovery, 10, p. 32 (Jan. 1949).

DARLINGTON, C. D. (1944). "Heredity, Development and Infection," Nature, 154, p. 164.

DARLINGTON, C. D. (1947). "A Revolution in Soviet Science." J. Hered, 38 (5), p. 143.

DARLINGTON, C. D. (1948). "The Plasmagene Theory of the Origin of Cancer." Brit. J. Cancer, 2, p. 118.

DARLINGTON, C. D. (1948 bis). "The Conflict Between Science and Society." (Conway Memorial Lecture). Watts & Co., London.

DOBZHANSKY, T. (1949). "The End of Genetics in the Soviet Union." Bull. Atom. Scientists, May, 1949.

GOLDSCHMIDT, R. (1949). "Research and Politics." Science, 109, p. 219.

HARLAND, S. C. (1949). Discovery, 10, p. 32 (Jan. 1949).

HASKELL, G. (1949). "Hybrid Corn (Maize) in Theory and Practice." The Biological Press, London.

HOGBEN, L. T. (1949). "The New Authoritarianism." (Conway Memorial Lecture). Watts & Co., London.

HUDSON, P. S., and RICHENS, R. H. (1936). "The New Genetics in the Soviet Union." Plant Breeding Abstracts, 16, p. 365.

HUXLEY, J. S. (1942). "Evolution, the Modern Synthesis" London and New York).

HUXLEY, J. S. (1945). Evolutionary Biology and related subjects [in the U.S.S.R.]." Nature, 156, p. 254.

HUXLEY, J. S. (1949). "Soviet Genetics : the Real Issue." Nature, 163, Nos. 4,155 and 4,156.

KAFTANOV, S. (1948). "In support of Michurin's Biological Theory in Higher Institutions of Learning." Izvestia, 8 . ix . 1948. (Verbatim translation in Science, 28 . i . 1949.

LANGDON-DAVIES, J. (1949). "Russia puts the Clock Back." Gollancz, London.

LEOPOLD, A. S. (1944). "The Nature of Heritable Wildness in Turkey." Condor, 46 (4), p. 133.

LYSENKO, T. D. (1943). "Heredity and its Variability." (Russian) ; English translation by Th. Dobzhansky, 1946, New York, Columbia Univ. Press).

LYSENKO, T. D. (1948). (Report and concluding remarks at the 1948 session of the Academy of Agricultural Sciences).
  (a) "Soviet Biology" (English), London. Birch Books, Ltd., New York, International Publishers, with title "The Science of Biology To-day."
  (b) In (²), Europe, 26, p. 30, p. 142. (French).

MULLER, H. J. (1948). "The Destruction of Science in the U.S.S.R., etc." Sat. Rev. Literature, 4 . xii . 48, p. 13 ; 11 . xii . 48, p. 8.

MULLER, H. J. (1949). "It still isn't a Science : a reply to George Bernard Shaw." Sat. Rev. Literature, 16 . iv . 49, p.11.

PEASE, D. C., and BAKER, R. F. (1949). "Preliminary Investigations of chromosomes and genes with the electron microscope." Science, 109, p. 8.

SHAW, G. B. (1949). "The Lysenko Muddle." Labour Monthly, (Jan. 1949) also (abbreviated) with title "Behind the Lysenko Controversy," in Sat. Rev. Literature, 16 . iv . 49, p. 10.

STERN, B. J. (1949). "Genetics Teaching and Lysenko," Science and Society, 13 (2), p. 136.

WADDINGTON, C. H. (1948-49). "Lysenko and the Scientists." New Statesman and Nation, 25 . xii . 48, p. 566, and 1 . i . 49 p.6.

WERTH, A. "Musical Uproar in Moscow," London, 1949.

WILSON, K. S. and WITTMER, C. L. (1946). "Stock-scion relationships in Tomatoes." Am. J. Bot., 33, p. 796.

INDEX

Made in Great Britain at the Pitman Press